Ten a

A.L.Gri...

OLIVER & BOYD

Oliver & Boyd
Robert Stevenson House
1-3 Baxter's Place
Leith Walk
Edinburgh EH1 3BB

A Division of Longman Group UK Ltd

ISBN 0 05 003927 X
First published 1987

Set in 12pt Linotype Melior Roman
Designed and illustrated by Scorpion Pica
Produced by Longman Group (FE) Ltd
Printed in Hong Kong

1

A **numeral** is a name for a number. We use the digits **1, 2, 3, 4, 5, 6, 7, 8 and 9**, together with **0**, to write numerals. We can also write a numeral in words.

For this number of drinking glasses we can write:

thirty-four or **34**.

1 Write in digits: seven hundred and eighty. 780

2 Write in digits: eight hundred and eight. 808

3 Write in digits: seven hundred and sixteen. 716

4 Write in words: 602. Six hundred and two.

5 Write in words: 444. Four hundred and forty four,

6 Write in words: 900. nine hundred,

Write in digits the number shown on each abacus.

7
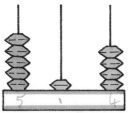
5 1 4

8
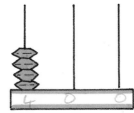
4 0 0

Write in words the number shown on each abacus.

9
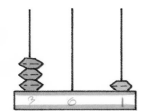
3 6 1

10
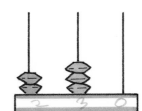
2 3 0

2

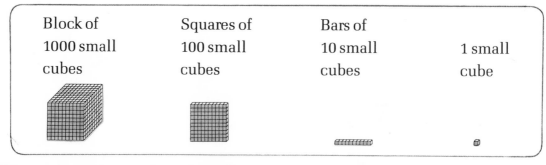

| Block of 1000 small cubes | Squares of 100 small cubes | Bars of 10 small cubes | 1 small cube |

Write in digits the number of small cubes in each of the pictures below.

1
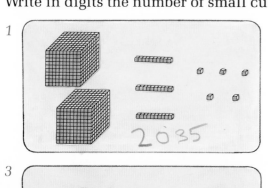
2035

2
2205

3
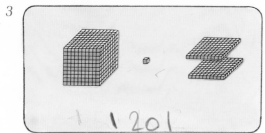
1201

4
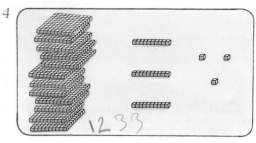
1233

Write these abacus numbers in words.

5
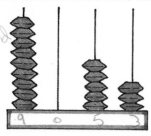

Ⓞ nine thausord and fifty three.

9 0 5 3

6
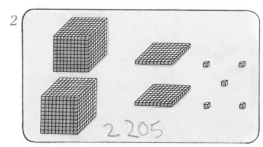

ninethoutre and te sea

9 0 6 ⊔

Write these meter readings in words.

7

| 1000s | 100s | 10s | 1s |

8

| 1000s | 100s | 10s | 1s |

January   3   0   8   0   34200
                              3080
April   4   2   Ø   Ø   0120

6   8   0   4

What is the total score on each dart board?

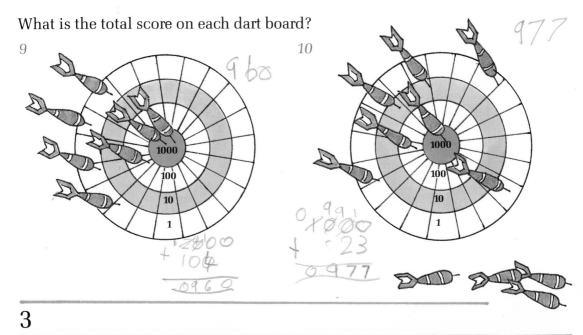

9

960

$$\begin{array}{r} 2800 \\ + 104 \\ \hline 0960 \end{array}$$

10

977

$$\begin{array}{r} 0 \times 000 \\ + 23 \\ \hline 0977 \end{array}$$

3

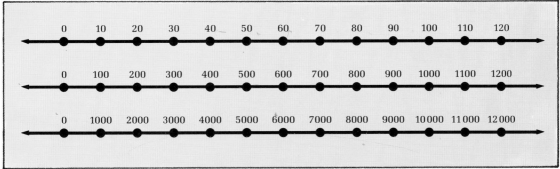

Use the number lines above to answer these questions.

1   What number is 70 more than 40?   *25*   *40*

2   What number is 30 less than 110?

3   What number is 500 greater than 600?   *100*

4   What number is 700 greater than 550?

5   What number is 600 less than 1200?   *700* *550*

6   What number is 3000 more than 8000?   *250*

7   What number is 5000 less than 11 000?

8   What number is 8000 more than 4000?

9   What number is 7000 less than 12 000?

10   What number is 9900 more than 3000?

4

Write each abacus number:

    a in digits.

    b in words.

five thous

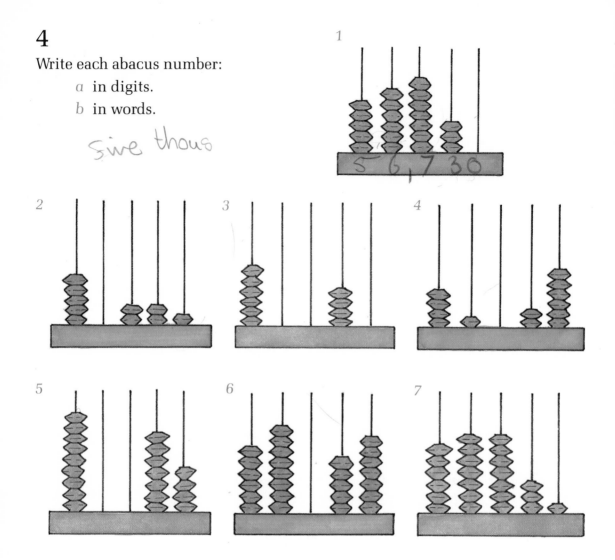

Build a numeral with:

8 7 in the hundreds place,

    3 in the tens place,

    0 in the thousands place,

    6 in the units place,

    5 in the ten thousands place.

9 4 in the thousands place,

    1 in the tens place,

    0 in the hundreds place,

    9 in the ten thousands place,

    7 in the units place.

10 Write the missing numerals.

15 998   16 001

5

Write these numerals in words.

1   101 101

2   100 000

3   111 001

4   101 010

5   110 011

6   111 100

7   101 100

8   100 011

9   111 111

10   110 001

6

Write each of these numerals using only digits.

1   909 thousand

2   80 thousand

3   600 thousand

4   five hundred and five thousand

5   18 thousand

6   What number is 1 more than 109 999?

7   What number is 10 more than 399 999?

8   What number is 100 less than 900 000?

9   What number is 1 less than 239 000?

10 With the digits 3, 0, 6, 1, 8, 5 name:

        a the smallest number possible.

        b the greatest number possible.

7

Write these abacus numbers in digits.

1
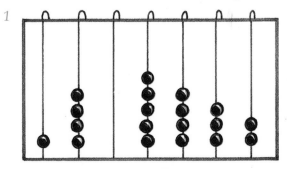

2
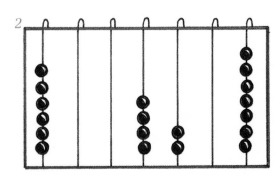

Write these calculator numbers in words.

3

4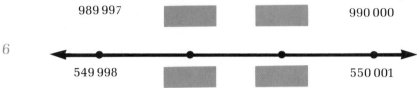

Write the missing numbers.

5

989 997 ▢ ▢ 990 000

6

549 998 ▢ ▢ 550 001

Build a numeral with:

7 5 in the hundreds place,
   9 in the units place,
   0 in the hundred thousands place,
   7 in the tens place,
   2 in the ten thousands place,
   4 in the millions place,
   1 in the thousands place.

8 3 in the thousands place,
   0 in the tens place,
   6 in the millions place,
   7 in the hundred thousands place,
   5 in the hundreds place,
   4 in the ten thousands place,
   8 in the units place.

9 Take 900 thousand from 9 million.

10 Add 500 000 to 5 million.

8

> The **expanded numeral** for 783 is
> 700 + 80 + 3.
> The expanded numeral for 7840 is
> 7000 + 800 + 40.
> The expanded numeral for 89 300 is
> 80 000 + 9000 + 300.

Write an expanded numeral for each of these.

1 7 080 740
2 7 400 550
3 1 001 010
4 3 901 070
5 5 670 085
6 10 400 706
7 7 004 609
8 2 025 430
9 1 623 000
10 9 030 400

9

Write in digits the number which is:

1   a hundred thousand more than a million.
2   a thousand more than a million.
3   a hundred more than a million.
4   ten more than a million.
5   ten thousand more than a million.
6   a hundred less than a million.
7   ten less than a million.
8   a thousand less than a million.
9   a million more than 39 963 939.
10 ten million more than 99 999 999.

10

In this space and scientific age we must understand large numbers.

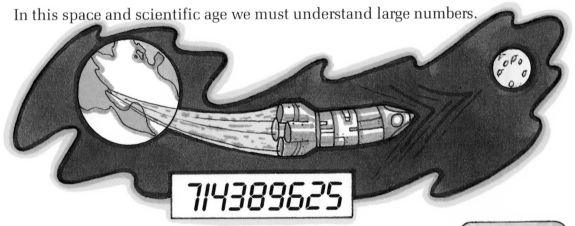

714389625

1   Which digit is in the hundred millions place?
2   Which digit is in the hundred thousands place?
3   In which place is the 1?
4   In which place is the 8?
5   Write this numeral in words.

404400400

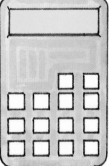

6   Write in digits seven hundred and seventy million, seven hundred and seven thousand.

7   Write in digits three hundred and forty-two million, nine hundred and thirty-four thousand, six hundred and seven.

8   Write in words 101 110 100.

9   Write in words 900 090 009.

10   Write in words 660 606 606.

11

An approximate number is sometimes good enough for our purposes, but it is important to state how accurate the approximate number is.

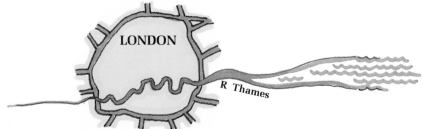

The population of London a few years ago was 8 186 836.

8 186 836

becomes 8 200 000 when rounded off to the nearest hundred thousand

and

becomes 8 000 000 when rounded off to the nearest million.

1   Round off 20 441 000 to the nearest hundred thousand.

2   Round off 32 546 000 to the nearest ten thousand.

3   Round off 199 970 000 to the nearest million.

4   Round off 99 118 000 to the nearest million.

5   Round off 9 581 000 to the nearest million.

6   Round off 49 824 000 to the nearest million.

7   Round off 6 071 000 to the nearest hundred thousand.

8   Round off 370 000 000 to the nearest hundred million.

9   Round off 404 000 000 to the nearest hundred million.

10   Round off 666 000 000 to the nearest ten million.

12

We have already learned that we can add
numbers in any order we like.

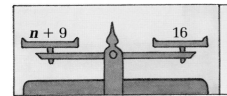

$3 + 1 + 4 = 8$ $3 + 1 + 4 = 8$ $3 + 1 + 4 = 8$

1   $22 + 16 + 18 = \blacksquare$
2   $28 + 93 + 7 = \blacksquare$
3   $77 + 27 + 3 + 3 = \blacksquare$
4   $45 + 18 + 25 = \blacksquare$
5   $38 + 9 + 11 + 12 = \blacksquare$
6   $6 + 9 + 7 + 24 = \blacksquare$
7   $360 + 150 + 50 = \blacksquare$
8   $80 + 90 + 60 + 20 = \blacksquare$
9   $769 + 500 + 5500 = \blacksquare$
10   $1600 + 946 + 400 = \blacksquare$

13

$n + 9$ 16

Solving equations
If $n + 9 = 16$, then $n = \blacksquare$.
$n = 7$ is the **solution.**

Solve these equations.

1   $n + 37 = 50$
2   $n + 9\frac{1}{2} = 20$
3   $21 + n = 40$
4   $35 + 45 = n$
5   $14 + a = 22$
6   $31 - n = 17$
7   $p - 17 = 30$
8   $r + 18 = 700$
9   $51 - a = 17$
10   $37 - x = 0$

You must
CHECK
each
solution.

14

$>$ means **is greater than**.
$<$ means **is less than**.

Write $>$, $<$ or $=$ in place of each ⬤.

1   $17 - 9$ ⬤ $6 + 2 + 0$
2   $86 + 5$ ⬤ $90 + 7$
3   $64 + 7$ ⬤ $8 + 63$
4   $60 + 36 + 40$ ⬤ $70 + 16 + 30$

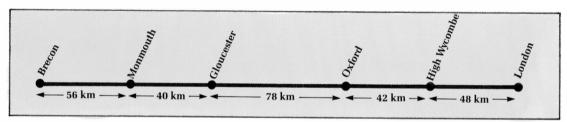
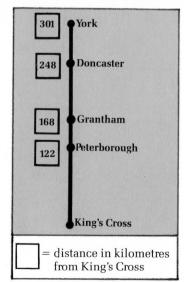

5   $10 + 217 + 190$ ⬤ $227 + 200 - 10$

6   $25 + 100 + 75$ ⬤ $300 - 40 - 60$

7   $324 - 9 - 6 - 1 - 4$ ⬤ $324 - 20$

8   $347 + 6 + 3 + 9 + 1 + 1$ ⬤ $370 - 5 - 5 - 4 - 6$

9   $810 - 30$ ⬤ $900 - 180$

10   $999 + 67 + 1$ ⬤ $1000 + 70$

15

Solve these equations.

1   $3500 - a = 2500$

2   $b + 800 = 4400$

3   $6500 - c = 900$

4   $2800 + d = 10\ 000$

5   $4030 + 5070 = e$

6   $40 + 10 + 50 + \blacksquare = 138$

7   $233 + 7 + 40 + \blacksquare = 320$

8   $435 + 4 - 2 + 6 - 7 - 1 = \blacksquare$

9   $4527 + 175 + 25 = \blacksquare$

10   $1480 + 120 = 2000 - n$

16

1   Work out the distance in kilometres from Gloucester to Brecon.

2   How far is it from Gloucester to High Wycombe?

3   How far is it from Monmouth to Oxford?

4   What is the distance from London to Gloucester?

5   How far is it from Monmouth to High Wycombe?

6   What is the distance from Grantham to Doncaster?

7   Work out the distance from Doncaster to York.

8   How far is it from Grantham to York?

9   How far is it from Peterborough to York?

10   What is the distance from Doncaster to Peterborough?

17

The Romans used seven basic numerals.

I	V	X	L	C	D	M
1	5	10	50	100	500	1000

$$CXVIII = 100 + 10 + 5 + 3 = 118$$

We subtract when the smaller numeral is on the left.

$$IV = 5 - 1 = 4 \qquad XC = 100 - 10 = 90$$

Write these in Roman numerals.

1   87   *2*   225   *3*   nine hundred and six

Write these in our numerals.

4   LXXXVIII   *5*   CXLVI   *6*   CCCLVI

Write these in our numerals.

7

MLXVI

8
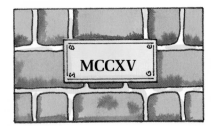
MCCXV

9

MCMLXIX

10

MDCCCLXXXVI

18

John had 15 marbles.
Tim had 8 marbles.
David had 7 marbles.

When they shared them equally,
John had 10 marbles,
Tim had 10 marbles,
David had 10 marbles.

The **average** of 15, 8 and 7 is **10**.

1   This table shows the number
of cars that passed a school
from 9.00 am to midday.
What was the average
number of cars an hour?

9-10	10-11	11-12
30	20	70

2   Work out the average of 17, 13, 14 and 16.

3   Karen spent an average of 50p a day during her five days' holiday. If she spent
60p on Monday, 40p on Tuesday, 34p on Wednesday and 66p on Thursday,
what did she spend on Friday?

4   The average of three numbers is 17. If the first number is 9 and the second 23,
what is the third number?

5   What is the average
weight of an apple?

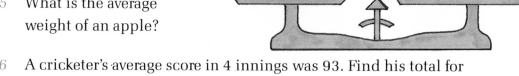

6   A cricketer's average score in 4 innings was 93. Find his total for
the 4 innings.

7   On each day of the week a motorist bought petrol. He bought these amounts:
15ℓ, 20ℓ, 20ℓ, 10ℓ, 25ℓ, 10ℓ, 40ℓ. What was the average purchased daily?

8   Find the average of 37, 20 and 63.

9   The average age of four children is 9 years. Peter is 8 years old and Ann is 6
years. Susan is the same age as Philip. How old is Philip?

10 What is the average cost of these kits?

FUN WITH MAGNETS £26

FINGERPRINT KIT £20

COLOUR SCIENCE £44

19

A bar chart can be used to show more than one set of information. This double bar chart shows the number of boy and girl swimmers in a school.

1 How many swimmers are there altogether in Year 1?

2 How many girl swimmers are there in the first two years?

3 How many boy swimmers are there in the 3rd and 4th years?

4 How many more boy swimmers than girl swimmers are there in Year 3 and Year 4 together?

5 How many more swimmers are there in Year 3 than Year 1?

This graph shows Sam's annual cycling record.

6 How far did he cycle during the last three months of the year?

7 How many more kilometres did he cycle in August than July?

8 How many more kilometres did he cycle in September than October?

9 What was the difference in kilometres between the highest and lowest recorded months?

10 In which month do you think the roads were blocked with snow?

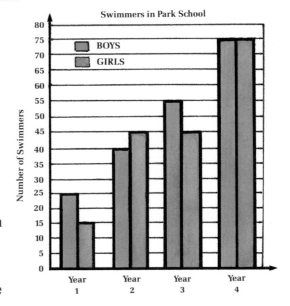

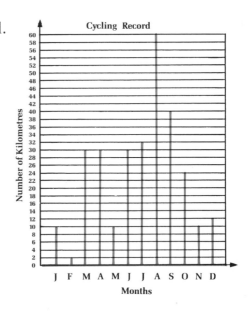

20

Find the missing factors or products in these equations.

1	$7 \times \blacksquare = 63$	2	$8 \times \blacksquare = 72$
3	$8 \times 7 = \blacksquare$	4	$48 \div \blacksquare = 12$
5	$\frac{81}{9} = \blacksquare$	6	$\blacksquare \times 10 = 100$
7	$42 = \blacksquare \times 7$	8	$4 \times 2 \times \blacksquare = 64$
9	$20 \times \blacksquare = 400$	10	$\frac{48}{\blacksquare} = 6$

21

We have already learned that we can add numbers in any order we like. We can also multiply numbers in any order which is convenient.

$②\times 7 \times ⑤ = 70 \quad ②\times ⑦\times 5 = 70 \quad 2 \times ⑦\times ⑤ = 70$

Find the products.

1	$4 \times 5 \times 7$	$= \blacksquare$	2	$25 \times 6 \times 4$	$= \blacksquare$
3	$2 \times 5 \times 33$	$= \blacksquare$	4	$6 \times 2 \times 9 \times 5$	$= \blacksquare$
5	$9 \times 5 \times 8$	$= \blacksquare$	6	$14 \times 5 \times 20$	$= \blacksquare$
7	$50 \times 9 \times 2$	$= \blacksquare$	8	$29 \times 5 \times 2$	$= \blacksquare$
9	$25 \times 39 \times 4 \times 10 = \blacksquare$		10	$2 \times 17 \times 50 \times 1 = \blacksquare$	

22

7×60	or	60×7	means	42 tens	=	420
3×900	or	900×3	means	27 hundreds	=	2700

1	$9 \times 80 = \blacksquare$	2	$700 \times 6 = \blacksquare$
3	$40 \times 9 = \blacksquare$	4	$700 \times 8 = \blacksquare$
5	$9 \times 900 = \blacksquare$	6	$5000 \times \blacksquare = 25\ 000$
7	$4900 \div 70 = \blacksquare$	8	$3600 \div 60 = \blacksquare$
9	$2000 \div 100 = \blacksquare$	10	$6400 \div 80 = \blacksquare$

23

We know that we can multiply factors in any order.
We also know that we can split factors.

$$25 \times 3 = (20 \times 3) + (5 \times 3) = 75$$

$$40 \times 70 = \textcircled{4} \times \textcircled{10} \times \textcircled{7} \times \textcircled{10} = 28 \times 100 = 2800$$

1   $80 \times 60 = \blacksquare$ 2 $70 \times 40 = \blacksquare$

3   $34 \times 3 = \blacksquare$ 4 $400 \times 50 = \blacksquare$

5   $5 \times 46 = \blacksquare$ 6 $3500 \div 70 = \blacksquare$

7   $\frac{6400}{80} = \blacksquare$ 8 $\blacksquare \times 100 = 6000$

9   $300 \times 300 = \blacksquare$ 10 $1800 \div 60 = \blacksquare$

24

Find the two numbers:

1   if their sum is 9 and their difference is 1.

2   if their sum is 16 and their difference 2.

3   if their difference is 7 and their sum is 31.

4   if their difference is 3 and their sum is 15.

5   if their product is 24 and their difference 5.

6   if their product is 48 and their sum 19.

7   if their difference is 7 and their product 30.

8   if their product is 32 and their quotient 2.

9   if their product is 36 and their quotient 1.

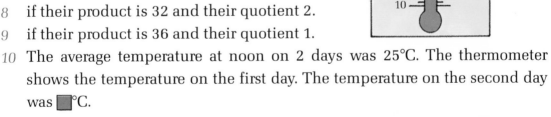

10 The average temperature at noon on 2 days was 25°C. The thermometer shows the temperature on the first day. The temperature on the second day was $\blacksquare$°C.

25

Find the number we can put in place of the letter in these equations.

1   $48 + 17 = (48 + 20) - a$

2   $47 + 38 = 50 + c$

3   $443 + 167 = (443 + 200) - n$

4    $(14 \times 20) - 14 = e \times 14$

5    $\frac{24\,000}{500} = r$

6    $\frac{16\,000}{250} = x$

7    $37 \times s = (37 \times 5) + (37 \times 60)$

8    $47 \times 31 = (50 \times 31) - (u \times 31)$

9    $73 \times k = (73 \times 100) - (\frac{73 \times 10}{2})$

10   $99 \times 568 = (99 \times 500) + (99 \times z) + (99 \times 8)$

26

When we use letters in place of numbers, we usually show multiplication without using the multiplication sign.

$$4b \text{ means } 4 \times b$$

$$4ab \text{ means } 4 \times a \times b$$

1   If $n = 9$, what is $6n + 7$?

2   If $a = 8$, what is $90 - 7a$?

3   If $p = 17$, what is $2p + 6$?

4   What is $80 \div 4d$, when $d = 4$?

5   What is $\frac{x}{6} + 12$, when $x = 48$?

If $a = 5$, $b = 7$ and $c = 2$:

6   $2b + 3c = \blacksquare$ 7 $abc = \blacksquare$

8   $6a - 3b = \blacksquare$ 9 $\frac{a}{b - c} = \blacksquare$

10   $\frac{a + b}{c} = \blacksquare$

27

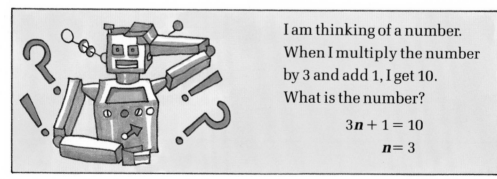

I am thinking of a number. When I multiply the number by 3 and add 1, I get 10. What is the number?

$$3n + 1 = 10$$
$$n = 3$$

Write an equation for each of these puzzles, and find a solution. Call the unknown number n.

1   I am thinking of a number. When I add 29 to it, I have 60. What is the number?

2   I am thinking of a number. When I subtract 95 from it, I have 905. What is the number?

3   I am thinking of a number. When I multiply it by 7, I have 630. What is the number?

4   Four times a number plus 3 is equal to 31. What is the number?

5   If 5 is subtracted from three times a number, the result is 19. Find the number.

6   I am thinking of a number. When 5 is subtracted from six times the number, the answer is 37. What is the number?

7   If I add 3 to twice a number, the result is 27. What is the number?

8   If 7 is added to $\frac{1}{3}$ of a number, the answer is 11. What is the number?

9   I am thinking of a number. If I multiply the number by 3, subtract 2 and divide by 4, the result is 4. What is the number?

10 I am thinking of a number. If I divide the number by 4 and add 7, the result is 15. What is the number?

28

Solve the equations below like this:

$$\frac{x}{5} = 3$$
$$x = 15$$

BE SURE TO CHECK EACH SOLUTION

1   $\frac{42}{n} + 2 = 8$

2   $\frac{96}{d} = 16$

3   $\frac{x}{9} = 6$

4   $17 - 5x = 2$

5   $7 + b = 53 - 8$

6   $3n - 3 = 24$

7   $t - 36 = 72$

8   $41d = 451$

9   $\frac{3}{4} + n = 3\frac{1}{2}$

10 $4x = 2x + 6$

29

1   $3n = 19 - 4$

2   $7x + 1 = 29$

3   $\frac{x}{7} + 6 = 9$

4   $3x + 2x + 1 = 21$

5   $4x = 10 - x$

6   $2 + 3d = 20$

7   $\frac{2n}{3} = 12$

8   $\frac{b}{2} + 7 = 15$

9   $\frac{2c}{7} = 2$

10   $5m - 7 = 18$

30

1   Write the correct sign ($>$, $<$ or $=$) in place of ◯.

    84 967 ◯ $(8 \times 10\ 000) + (4 \times 100) + 967$

2   Find the missing factor in this equation.

    $19 \times$ ■ $\times 4 = 1900$

3   Write the number which has been covered in this subtraction.

$$\begin{array}{r} \blacksquare\blacksquare\blacksquare\blacksquare \\ -\ 1\ 0\ 1 \\ \hline 1\ 1\ 0\ 0 \end{array}$$

4   $(28 \times 7) + (3 \times 28) =$ ■

5   An average of 40 planes an hour left Heathrow Airport during twenty-four hours. How many planes left altogether?

6   Write this in full.

    $100 = (16 \times$ ■$) + 36$

7   What number would you get when you divide the product of 32 and 7 by 8?

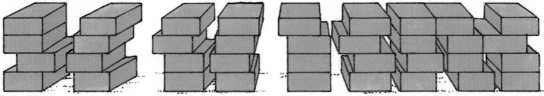

8   There is a total of three thousand six hundred pencils in the boxes above. Each box holds the same number. How many pencils are in a box?

9   $2\frac{1}{3} \times 9 =$ ■

10   The average of $4\frac{1}{2}$, $1\frac{1}{2}$ and 6 is ■.

31

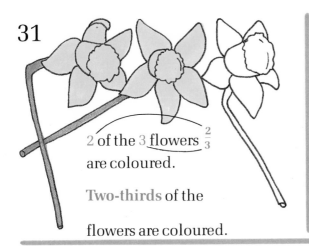

2 of the 3 flowers $\frac{2}{3}$
are coloured.

Two-thirds of the

flowers are coloured.

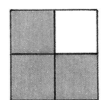

In this square 3 of the
4 parts are coloured.

$\frac{3}{4}$ (three-quarters)

Write a fraction to show:

    a the coloured part of each set or shape

    b the uncoloured part.

1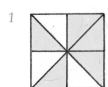

2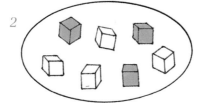

3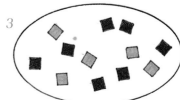

4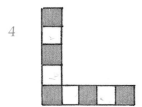

5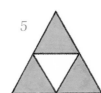

6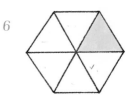

7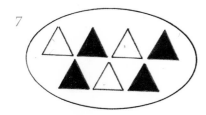

8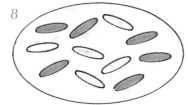

9

10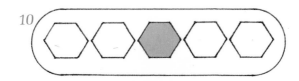

32

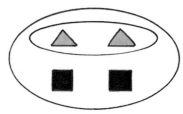

We can see that 2 of the 4 shapes, that is $\frac{2}{4}$, are coloured.

We can also see that 1 of the 2 sets of shapes, that is $\frac{1}{2}$, are triangles.

$\frac{2}{4}$ is **equivalent** to $\frac{1}{2}$

$\frac{2}{4} = \frac{1}{2}$

Write two equivalent fractions for each of the pictures below.

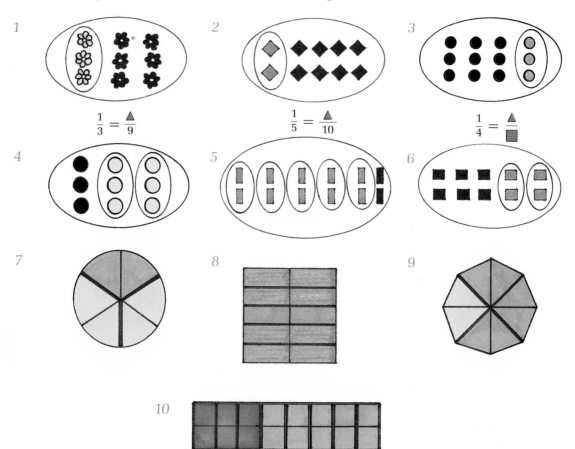

33

$$\frac{1}{5} \text{ of } 10 = 2$$

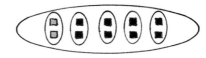

$$\frac{3}{5} \text{ of } 10 = 3 \times 2 = 6$$

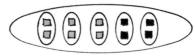

1   $\frac{1}{7}$ of 35 = ▨

2   $\frac{1}{9}$ of 270 = ▨

3   $\frac{1}{8}$ of 400 = ▨

4   $\frac{1}{4}$ of 48 is 12

       so $\frac{3}{4}$ of 48 = ▨

5   $\frac{1}{7}$ of 56 is 8,

     so $\frac{5}{7}$ of 56 = ▨

6   $\frac{3}{5}$ of 60 = ▨

7   $\frac{5}{8}$ of 64 = ▨

8   $\frac{2}{3}$ of 450 = ▨

9   $\frac{5}{8}$ of 720 = ▨

10   $\frac{4}{5}$ of 600 = ▨

34

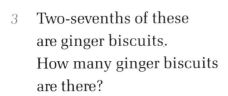

A   B   D

1   What fraction of **AD** is **AB?**

2   What price was
paid for the rugby
ball?

£18.90

SALE
$\frac{1}{3}$
OFF MARKED PRICE

3   Two-sevenths of these
are ginger biscuits.
How many ginger biscuits
are there?

4   Three-eighths of these
eggs are brown. How many
white eggs are there?

1 DOZEN EGGS

1 DOZEN EGGS

5 After three-quarters of this ball of string have been used, what length remains?

6 How much is $\frac{2}{3}$ of this money?

7 What fraction of a day is 3 hours?

8 Ali lost a fifth of his marbles. If he still had 20 left, how many did he have at first?

9 Four-fifths of Rani's money is 80p. How much does she have?

10 There are 40 litres of water in this tank. How many litres will it hold when full?

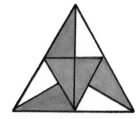

35

1 Write in digits the numeral for a thousand million.

2 Solve this equation: $\frac{100}{n}$ = 7 remainder 9.

3 From the sum of 198 and 102, subtract the product of 25 and 8.

4 Find the number which can be put in place of ■.

$$78 + ■ = 3 \times 78$$

5 From what number can 9 be subtracted 9 times, leaving a remainder of 9?

6 ($\frac{1}{4}$ of 64) $\times$ ($\frac{1}{9} \times$ 27) = ■

7 Write the letter of the sentence which is true.

  a $225 \div 15 < 260 \div 20$

  b $225 \div 15 = 260 \div 20$

  c $225 \div 15 > 260 \div 20$

8 What fraction of the shape is:

  a coloured?

  b not coloured?

9   156 is the product of three factors. Two of the factors are 13 and 4.
What is the other factor?

10 Four children completed a jigsaw
puzzle and recorded their time in
minutes. What was the average time?

Ann	17
Tim	12
Bob	8
Jane	23

36

These pictures show that $\frac{1}{2}, \frac{2}{4}, \frac{3}{6}, \frac{4}{8}, \frac{5}{10}$ are **equivalent fractions**
This means that they are names for the same part or fraction.

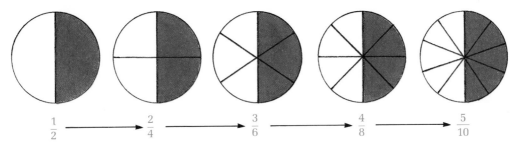

$$\frac{1}{2} \longrightarrow \frac{2}{4} \longrightarrow \frac{3}{6} \longrightarrow \frac{4}{8} \longrightarrow \frac{5}{10}$$

equivalent fractions

Complete these.

1  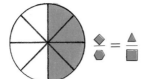 $\frac{\Diamond}{\hexagon} = \frac{\triangle}{\blacksquare}$

2 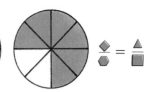 $\frac{\Diamond}{\hexagon} = \frac{\triangle}{\blacksquare}$

3 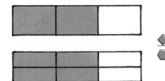 $\frac{\Diamond}{\hexagon} = \frac{\triangle}{\blacksquare}$

4 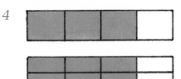 $\frac{\Diamond}{\hexagon} = \frac{\triangle}{\blacksquare}$

Write the next two fractions for each of these sets.

5 $\left\{ \frac{1}{3}, \frac{2}{6}, \frac{3}{9}, \frac{4}{12}, \frac{a}{b}, \frac{c}{d} \cdots \right\}$

6 $\left\{ \frac{2}{5}, \frac{4}{10}, \frac{6}{15}, \frac{8}{20}, \frac{10}{25}, \frac{r}{s}, \frac{x}{y}, \cdots \right\}$

7 $\frac{1}{4} = \frac{\triangle}{8} = \frac{3}{\blacksquare}$

8 $\frac{3}{5} = \frac{\triangle}{10} = \frac{9}{\blacksquare}$

9 $\frac{12}{16} = \frac{\Diamond}{8}$

10 $\frac{20}{24} = \frac{\Diamond}{6}$

37

Look at the examples below.

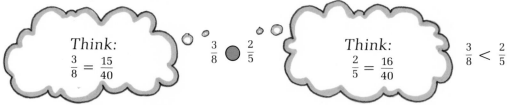

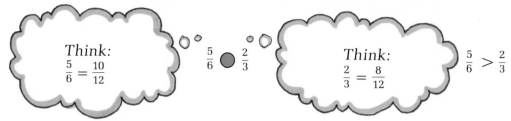

Write the correct sign (>, < or =) in place of each ⬤.

1. $\frac{7}{9}$ ⬤ $\frac{2}{3}$ 2. $\frac{3}{5}$ ⬤ $\frac{5}{9}$

3. $\frac{4}{5}$ ⬤ $\frac{8}{10}$ 4. $\frac{1}{8}$ ⬤ $\frac{2}{11}$

5. $\frac{5}{8}$ ⬤ $\frac{11}{16}$ 6. $\frac{5}{7}$ ⬤ $\frac{17}{21}$

7. $\frac{3}{7}$ ⬤ $\frac{5}{14}$ 8. $\frac{7}{10}$ ⬤ $\frac{4}{5}$

9. $\frac{3}{4}$ ⬤ $\frac{2}{3}$ 10. $\frac{2}{3}$ ⬤ $\frac{7}{8}$

38

$$\left\{\frac{2}{6}, \frac{1}{3}, \frac{3}{9}, \frac{4}{12}, \ldots\right\}$$

The simplest fraction in this set of equivalent fractions is $\frac{1}{3}$. When a fraction is in its simplest form, we say it is in its **lowest terms**.

Write the fraction which is in its lowest terms in each of these sets of equivalent fractions.

1. $\left\{\frac{4}{16}, \frac{5}{20}, \frac{1}{4}, \frac{3}{12}, \frac{6}{24}, \ldots\right\}$

2. $\left\{\frac{2}{3}, \frac{8}{12}, \frac{20}{30}, \frac{6}{9}, \frac{12}{18}, \ldots\right\}$

3. $\left\{\frac{9}{15}, \frac{6}{10}, \frac{3}{5}, \frac{15}{25}, \frac{30}{50}, \ldots\right\}$

$4 \ \{ \frac{10}{20}, \frac{9}{18}, \frac{3}{6}, \frac{1}{2}, \frac{4}{8}, \dots \}$

$5 \ \{ \frac{3}{18}, \frac{15}{90}, \frac{1}{6}, \frac{2}{12}, \frac{5}{30}, \dots \}$

In each of the sets below, the fraction in its lowest terms is covered by ■.

Write each of these covered fractions.

$6 \ \{ ■, \frac{6}{16}, \frac{9}{24}, \frac{24}{64}, \dots \}$

$7 \ \{ ■, \frac{8}{10}, \frac{12}{15}, \frac{16}{30}, \dots \}$

$8 \ \{ ■, \frac{16}{18}, \frac{24}{27}, \frac{32}{36}, \dots \}$

$9 \ \{ ■, \frac{6}{14}, \frac{9}{21}, \frac{12}{28}, \dots \}$

$10 \ \{ ■, \frac{10}{12}, \frac{15}{18}, \frac{20}{24}, \dots \}$

39

To reduce (bring) $\frac{24}{36}$ to its lowest terms:

> Think: **numerator** → 24 (factors 1, 2, 3, 4, 6, 8, ⑫)
>
> **denominator** → 36 (factors 1, 2, 3, 4, 6, 9, ⑫)

Highest factor in numerator and denominator (**common factor**) is 12.

$$\frac{\overset{2}{\cancel{24}}}{\underset{3}{\cancel{36}}}$$ The crossed-out figures have been **cancelled**.

$\frac{24}{36}$ in its lowest terms is $\frac{2}{3}$.

Reduce these fractions to their lowest terms.

1   $\frac{15}{35} = \frac{\triangle}{7}$ 2 $\frac{30}{40} = \frac{3}{■}$ 3 $\frac{36}{48} = \frac{\triangle}{■}$

4   $\frac{14}{42}$ 5 $\frac{36}{40}$ 6 $\frac{30}{54}$

7   $\frac{54}{63}$ 8 $\frac{16}{36}$ 9 $\frac{95}{100}$

10   $\frac{600}{1000}$

40

1 How many thousands are there in $2\frac{1}{2}$ million?
2 $99 \times 1 \times 15 = $
3 $100 \times 100 \times 100$. Write the product in words.
4 I am thinking of a certain number. Two-thirds of the number is 30. What is the number?

5 A school hall has 24 rows of chairs with 25 chairs in a row. How many chairs are there?

6 Write and solve an equation for this problem. *Seven times a number is equal to the sum of 19 and 37. What is the number?*

7 What is the average of the temperatures shown by these thermometers? Give your answer in degrees Celsius, like this : ■°C.

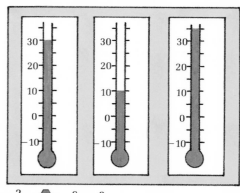

8 Write out this statement in full: $\frac{2}{3} = \frac{⬟}{6} = \frac{6}{◆} = \frac{8}{▲}$
9 Find $\frac{1}{100}$ of eleven thousand one hundred.
10 Write a fraction in its lowest terms to show:
       a the part of the shape which is coloured,
       b the part of the shape which is not coloured.

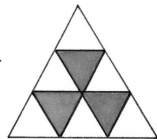

41

Numbers like $2\frac{1}{2}$, $4\frac{1}{4}$, $9\frac{2}{5}$ . . . are called **mixed numbers** – one part names a whole number, the other a fraction.

Write a mixed number for each of these.

1 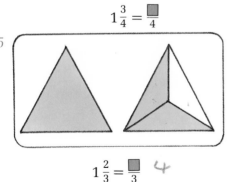 $1\frac{3}{1}$

2 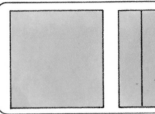 $1\frac{3}{4}$

Use the drawings below to help you to write the equations in full.

3

$1\frac{3}{4}$

$$1\frac{3}{4} = \frac{\blacksquare}{4}$$

4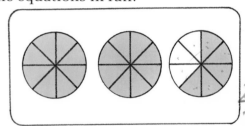

$2\frac{5}{8}$

$$2\frac{5}{8} = \frac{\blacksquare}{8}$$

5 $\frac{2}{3}$

$$1\frac{2}{3} = \frac{\blacksquare}{3} \quad 4$$

6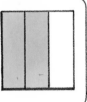

$$2\frac{2}{3} = \frac{\blacksquare}{3}$$

$2\frac{2}{3}$

7    $3\frac{9}{10} = \frac{\blacksquare}{10}$

8    $4\frac{7}{8} = \frac{\blacksquare}{8}$

9    $4\frac{4}{5} = \frac{\blacksquare}{5}$

10    $10\frac{1}{2} = \frac{\blacksquare}{2}$

42

> When the numerator is greater than the denominator,
> the fractions are called **improper fractions**.
>
> $$\frac{13}{4} \qquad \frac{9}{6} \qquad \frac{6}{5} \qquad \frac{101}{2}$$

Write these improper fractions as mixed numbers.

1 $\frac{17}{2}$ 　　2 $\frac{9}{8}$ 　　3 $\frac{23}{7}$

Write these improper fractions as whole numbers.

4 $\frac{24}{3}$ 　　5 $\frac{42}{7}$ 　　6 $\frac{18}{6}$

Write these mixed numbers as improper fractions.

7 $3\frac{4}{7}$ 　　8 $9\frac{6}{11}$ 　　9 $10\frac{1}{10}$

10 Sort the fractions below into two sets:

　　　　a improper fractions,

　　　　b proper fractions.

$$\frac{3}{2} \qquad \frac{19}{3} \qquad \frac{4}{9} \qquad \frac{7}{3} \qquad \frac{18}{2} \qquad \frac{7}{14}$$

43

> **Remember!**
> Answers should be written in their **lowest terms**
> and improper fractions changed to **mixed numbers**.

Find the sums or differences.

1 $\frac{3}{5} + \frac{1}{5} = \frac{\blacksquare}{5}$ 　　　　　　　　　2 $\frac{7}{9} - \frac{2}{9} = \frac{\blacksquare}{9}$

3 $\frac{5}{9} + \frac{2}{9} = \frac{\blacksquare}{9}$ 　　　　　　　　　4 $\frac{11}{12} - \frac{5}{12} = \frac{\blacksquare}{12} = \frac{\blacktriangle}{2}$

5 $1 - \frac{3}{11} = \frac{\blacksquare}{11}$ 　　　　　　　　　6 $\frac{5}{12} + \frac{11}{12}$

7 $\frac{3}{5} + \frac{3}{5}$ 　　　　　　　　　　　　　8 $1 - \frac{7}{10}$

9 $\frac{3}{8} + \frac{5}{8}$ 　　　　　　　　　　　　　10 $1\frac{3}{10} - \frac{9}{10}$

44

> To find the sum of $\frac{1}{3}$ and $\frac{1}{4}$,
>
> or the difference between $\frac{1}{3}$ and $\frac{1}{4}$,
>
> we can change $\frac{1}{3}$ to twelfths $(\frac{4}{12})$
>
> and we can change $\frac{1}{4}$ to twelfths $(\frac{3}{12})$
>
> then add: $\frac{4}{12} + \frac{3}{12} = \frac{7}{12}$
>
> or subtract: $\frac{4}{12} - \frac{3}{12} = \frac{1}{12}$

Find the sums or differences.

1   $\frac{1}{5} + \frac{1}{10} = \frac{\blacksquare}{10}$ 2 $\frac{1}{3} - \frac{1}{6} = \frac{\blacksquare}{6}$

3   $\frac{1}{4} + \frac{1}{8}$ 4 $\frac{1}{2} - \frac{1}{3}$

5   $\frac{1}{8} + \frac{1}{12}$ 6 $\frac{2}{3} + \frac{3}{4}$

7   $\frac{1}{2} + \frac{3}{5}$ 8 $\frac{4}{5} - \frac{3}{10}$

9   $\frac{7}{8} - \frac{1}{2}$ 10 $\frac{5}{9} + \frac{2}{3}$

45

1   Write in digits the number which is fifty thousand more than fifty million.

2   Divide the product of 24 and 13 by 4.

3   If 6 ■ 8 is exactly divisible by 9, what digit must be put in place of ■ ?

4   What fraction of a day is sixteen hours? (Remember to write answers in their lowest terms.)

5   What is the average number of cherries in a set?

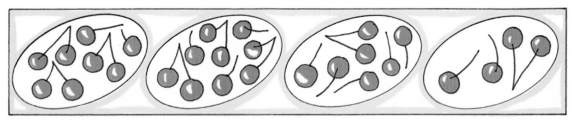

34

6   Look at the pattern of the numbers in the sequence below.
Write the next two numbers.

1, 4, 2, 8, 3, 12, 4, ■, ■

7   Look at the shaded parts of the shapes then write the equation in full.

$$\frac{5}{\blacksquare} = \frac{\hexagon}{12}$$

8   Who am I? If you subtract me from $\frac{1}{2}$, you have $\frac{3}{8}$.

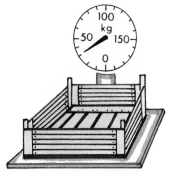 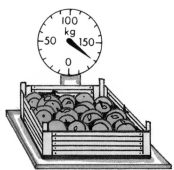

9   What is the weight of the apples?

10   What is the sum of all the factors of 24 (not including 1 and 24)?

46

We add three fractions in the same way
as we add two fractions.

$$\frac{1}{3} + \frac{1}{6} + \frac{1}{2} = \frac{2}{6} + \frac{1}{6} + \frac{3}{6} = \frac{6}{6} = 1$$

Add these.

1   $\frac{1}{2} + \frac{1}{4} + \frac{1}{8}$ 2 $\frac{1}{3} + \frac{1}{2} + \frac{2}{3}$

3   $\frac{3}{10} + \frac{1}{2} + \frac{1}{10}$ 4 $\frac{3}{8} + \frac{1}{4} + \frac{1}{8}$

5   $\frac{1}{2} + \frac{1}{8} + \frac{3}{8}$ 6 $\frac{5}{8} + \frac{1}{4} + \frac{3}{8}$

7   $1\frac{1}{2} + 2\frac{3}{4} + 1\frac{1}{4}$ 8 $3\frac{1}{8} + 4\frac{1}{4} + 1\frac{3}{8}$

9   $2\frac{3}{5} + 1\frac{2}{5} + \frac{1}{5}$ 10 $3\frac{2}{3} + 7\frac{3}{4} + 1\frac{1}{3}$

47

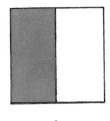

$\frac{1}{2}$

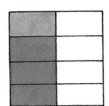

$\frac{1}{4}$ of $\frac{1}{2}$ =

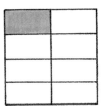

$\frac{1}{8}$

or

$\frac{1}{4} \times \frac{1}{2}$ = $\frac{1}{8}$

Complete these equations.

1

$\frac{1}{2}$

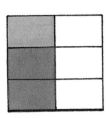

$\frac{1}{3}$ of $\frac{1}{2} = \dfrac{\blacktriangle}{\blacksquare}$

2

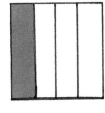

$\frac{1}{4}$

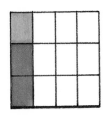

$\frac{1}{3} \times \frac{1}{4} = \dfrac{\blacklozenge}{\hexagon}$

3 $\frac{1}{5}$ of $\frac{1}{3} = \dfrac{\blacklozenge}{\hexagon}$

5 $\frac{1}{2} \times \frac{1}{5} = \dfrac{\blacktriangle}{\blacksquare}$

4 $\frac{1}{3} \times \frac{1}{3} = \dfrac{\blacklozenge}{\hexagon}$

6 $\frac{1}{5} \times \frac{1}{2} = \dfrac{\blacktriangle}{\blacksquare}$

$$\frac{3}{8} \text{ of } \frac{1}{2} \text{ or } \frac{3}{8} \times \frac{1}{2} = \frac{3}{16} \qquad \frac{\text{(product of 3 and 1)}}{\text{(product of 8 and 2)}}$$

Now work out these examples.

7 $\frac{3}{7} \times \frac{1}{2} = \dfrac{\blacksquare}{14}$

9 $\frac{3}{5} \times \frac{2}{5}$

8 $\frac{2}{3}$ of $\frac{4}{5} = \dfrac{8}{\blacksquare}$

10 $\frac{1}{7} \times \frac{3}{4}$

48

Study these two methods of working.

Divide the product of 17 and 24 by 8.

$$\frac{17 \times 24}{8} = \frac{408}{8} = 51$$

$$\frac{17 \times \overset{3}{\cancel{24}}}{\cancel{8}_{1}} = 51$$

It is much easier to divide 24 by 8 first.

1 $\dfrac{19 \times 16}{4} = \blacksquare$

2 $\dfrac{\overset{69}{\cancel{276}}}{1} \times \dfrac{3}{\cancel{4}_{1}} = \blacksquare$

3 $\dfrac{9 \times 63}{7} = \blacksquare$

4 $\dfrac{6 \times 48}{8} = \blacksquare$

5 $48 \times \dfrac{9}{16} = \blacksquare$

6 $\dfrac{3}{5} \times 100 = \blacksquare$

7 Divide the product of 19 and 18 by 6.

8 Find one-fifth of the product of 35 and 8.

9 $(36 \times 17) \div 12 = \blacksquare$

10 $\dfrac{1}{9}$ of $(48 \times 27) = \blacksquare$

49

1 Change these mixed numbers to improper fractions.

   a $3\frac{5}{8}$ b $7\frac{9}{10}$ c $5\frac{5}{9}$

2 Reduce these fractions to their lowest terms.

   a $\frac{20}{72}$ b $\frac{18}{48}$ c $\frac{24}{96}$

3 $45 \times \dfrac{13}{15} = \blacksquare$

4 Find the product of $4\frac{1}{2}$ and 16.

5 $\dfrac{3}{4}$ of $\dfrac{4}{9} = \dfrac{\blacklozenge}{\hexagon}$

6 Solve this equation:

$$\frac{3}{4} + \frac{1}{2} + \frac{1}{3} = \frac{\hexagon}{12} + \frac{\blacklozenge}{12} + \frac{\blacktriangle}{12} = \boldsymbol{n}$$

7   Find the difference between $1\frac{1}{4}$ and $\frac{7}{8}$.

8   Write $>$, $<$ or $=$ in place of ● in this statement.

$$\frac{11}{16} \bullet \frac{5}{8}$$

9   Half of $\frac{1}{3} = \frac{\bullet}{\blacklozenge}$ 10 $4 \div 9 = \frac{\blacktriangle}{\bullet}$

50

1   In 1975 the population of a city was 2 070 600. By 1985 the population had increased by thirty thousand four hundred. Write in digits the population of the city in 1985.

2   Round off 10 060 000 to the nearest hundred thousand.

3   Complete this statement.

      The product of 40 and 50 is equal to the sum of 50 and ■.

4   $3\frac{1}{4} \times 24 = $ ■

5   Look at this set of equivalent fractions.

$$\left\{ \frac{3}{4} , \frac{6}{8} , \frac{9}{12} , \frac{12}{16} , \cdots \right\}$$

Now write the next two fractions in the set.

6   What fraction of this rectangle is coloured:

       a blue?   b red?   c yellow?

7   There are 24 pupils or $\frac{8}{9}$ of the class present. How many pupils are in the class?

8   Tom set out to walk home from school. After he had walked $1\frac{1}{2}$ km his mother gave him a lift. How far did he travel by car?

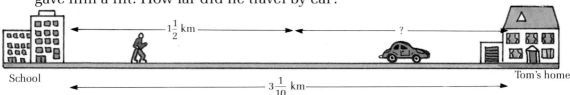

9   Write $>$, $<$ or $=$ in place of ● in this statement.

       $2 \times 555 \bullet 5 \times 222$

10 Raja gave John $\frac{1}{3}$ of his picture stickers. John received 27 stickers. How many stickers does Raja have now?

51

On this abacus the point separates the whole
numbers from the fractions. We can write this
abacus number in two ways:

$$32\tfrac{7}{10} \text{ or } 32{\cdot}7.$$

(We say **thirty-two point seven**.)

32·7 is a **decimal fraction**.

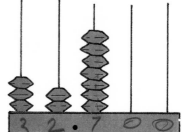

The number shown on this
abacus is $32\tfrac{7}{100}$ or 32·07.
(We say **thirty-two point
nought seven**.)

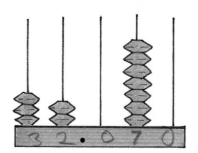

The number shown on this
abacus is $32\tfrac{7}{1000}$ or 32·007.
(We say **thirty-two point
nought nought seven**.)

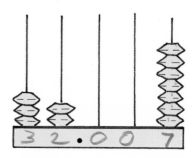

Write these abacus numbers as decimal fractions.

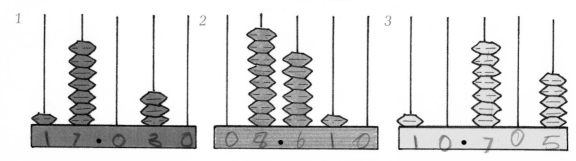

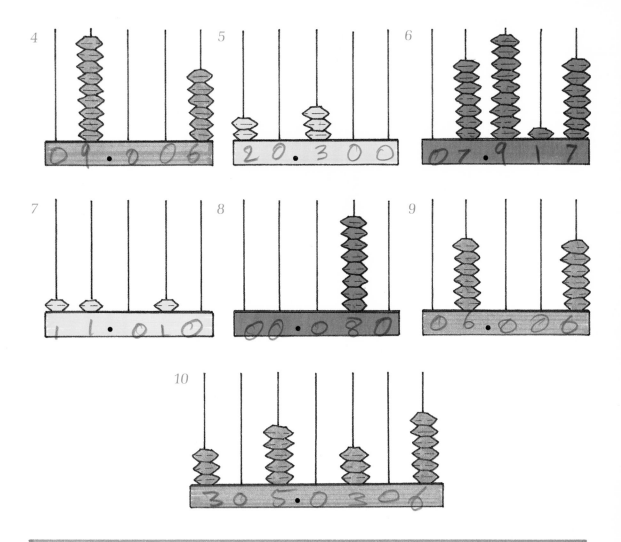

4   0 9 . 0 0 6

5   2 0 . 3 0 0

6   0 7 . 9 1 7

7   1 1 . 0 1 0

8   0 0 . 0 8 0

9   0 6 . 0 0 6

10   3 0 5 . 0 3 0

52

1   Which of the numerals below means 7 tenths?

     7·0   0·007   0·07   0·0007   0·7

2   Which of the numerals below means 3 hundredths?

     0·003   0·3   0·0003   3·0   0·03

3   Which of the numerals below means 9 thousandths?

     9·0   0·09   0·009   0·0009

4   In which of the numerals below does the 8 mean 8 thousandths?

     8·762   0·783   7·008   6·3958

Look at these examples.

$$5 \cdot 297 = 5 + \frac{2}{10} + \frac{9}{100} + \frac{7}{1000} = 5\,\frac{297}{1000}$$

$$6 \cdot 009 = 6 + \frac{9}{1000} = 6\,\frac{9}{1000}$$

Now write these in the same way.

5   $4 \cdot 38 = 4 + \dfrac{\hexagon}{10} + \dfrac{\triangledown}{100} = 4\,\dfrac{\blacksquare}{100}$

6   $7 \cdot 01 = 7 + \dfrac{\triangledown}{100} = 7\,\dfrac{\blacksquare}{100}$

7   $9 \cdot 376 = 9 + \dfrac{\hexagon}{10} + \dfrac{\triangledown}{100} + \dfrac{\triangle}{1000} = 9\,\dfrac{\blacksquare}{1000}$

8   $4 \cdot 003 = 4 + \dfrac{\triangle}{1000} = 4\,\dfrac{\blacksquare}{1000}$

9   $7 \cdot 078 = 7 + \dfrac{\triangledown}{100} + \dfrac{\triangle}{1000} = 7\,\dfrac{\blacksquare}{1000}$

10   $0 \cdot 703 = \dfrac{\hexagon}{10} + \dfrac{\triangle}{1000} = \dfrac{\blacksquare}{1000}$

53

Look at these examples.

$$4\,\frac{7}{10} = 4 \cdot 7 \qquad\qquad \frac{29}{1000} = 0 \cdot 029$$

Now write these in decimal form.

1   $4\,\dfrac{3}{10}$ 2 $5\,\dfrac{7}{100}$ 3 $8\,\dfrac{9}{1000}$

4   $\dfrac{37}{100}$ 5 $\dfrac{3}{1000}$ 6 $\dfrac{24}{1000}$

7   $4\,\dfrac{2}{1000}$ 8 $17\,\dfrac{23}{100}$ 9 $\dfrac{40}{1000}$

10   $\dfrac{237}{100}$

54

Write out each of the statements below, putting in the correct sign (>, < or =) in place of each ⬤.

1 2·200 ⬤ 2·2
2 2·02 ⬤ 2·2
3 2·002 ⬤ 2·02
4 0·03 ⬤ 0·021
5 0·17 ⬤ 0·5
6 0·4 ⬤ 0·36
7 9·009 ⬤ 8·767
8 3·004 ⬤ 3·012
9 0·701 ⬤ 1·0
10 0·304 ⬤ 1·104

55

1 Write <, > or = in place of each ⬤.
  a XCIX ⬤ 99
  b XLIX ⬤ LXIX
2 What is the largest number that can be named with a four-digit numeral that has 0 as one of its digits?
3 $3500 - \blacksquare = 3000 - 90$
4 Write this equation in full: $\frac{3}{8} = \frac{12}{\blacksquare}$.
5 Study these fractions:
   $\frac{3}{4}$ $\frac{7}{8}$ $\frac{8}{16}$ $\frac{1}{5}$ $\frac{6}{15}$ $\frac{1}{4}$ $\frac{2}{4}$
   From these write out all the fractions that are equivalent to:
   a $\frac{1}{2}$
   b $\frac{2}{5}$

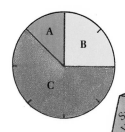

The pie chart shows how the 24 pupils in a class were graded for swimming.

6 How many pupils were in Grade A?
7 How many pupils were in Grade B?
8 How many pupils were in Grade C?
9 A car uses 12 litres of petrol in travelling 100 km. How many litres will be used on a journey of 350 km?
10 Sue and Peter each bought a model set for a total of £12. What would have been the usual price of one model set?

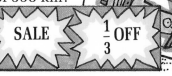

SALE $\frac{1}{3}$ OFF

56

> We can show that $0 \cdot 75 = \frac{3}{4}$ by writing $0 \cdot 75$ as
>
> $\frac{75}{100}$ and reducing $\overset{3}{\underset{4}{\cancel{\frac{75}{100}}}}$ to its **lowest terms**.

Write these as fractions in their lowest terms.

1	0·5	0·25	*2*	0·2	0·6
3	0·4	0·8	*4*	0·15	0·45
5	0·05	0·95	*6*	0·85	0·55
7	0·65	0·85	*8*	0·125	0·375
9	0·625	0·875	*10*	0·425	0·175

57

$$0 \cdot 7 + 0 \cdot 5 = 1 \cdot 2$$

0 0·1 0·2 0·3 0·4 0·5 0·6 0·7 0·8 0·9 1·0 1·1 1·2 1·3 1·4 1·5 1·6 1·7 1·8

Use the number line above to help you with these additions and subtractions.

1	0·6 + 0·3		*2*	0·7 + 0·5
3	0·6 + 0·9		*4*	0·8 + 0·8
5	1·2 + 0·5		*6*	0·9 − 0·3
7	1·1 − 0·7		*8*	1·7 − 0·9
9	1·0 − 0·4		*10*	1·6 − 0·8

58

Study the examples below.

> $\frac{17}{100} + \frac{11}{100} = \frac{28}{100} \rightarrow 0 \cdot 17 + 0 \cdot 11 = 0 \cdot 28$
>
> $\frac{44}{100} - \frac{18}{100} = \frac{26}{100} \rightarrow 0 \cdot 44 - 0 \cdot 18 = 0 \cdot 26$

Find the sums.

1 0·47 + 0·32

2 0·61 + 0·09

3 0·76 + 0·15

4   0·45 + 0·08
5   0·09 + 0·06

Find the differences

6   0·43 − 0·12
7   0·53 − 0·06
8   7·36 − 0·19
9   0·47 − 0·28
10 4·36 − 0·97

59

If you really understand decimals, you will find these very easy.

Find the sums.

1   0·147 + 0·4
2   0·177 + 0·5
3   0·4 + 0·019
4   0·06 + 0·631
5   1·08 + 1·19

Find the differences.

6   0·15 − 0·08
7   0·01 − 0·001
8   0·016 − 0·006
9   0·142 − 0·099
10 0·798 − 0·09

60

1   The distance from the Earth to the Sun is about one hundred and fifty million kilometres. Write this numeral in digits.

2   Find the sum of 639, 650 and 350.

3   Write out this addition in full.

$$\begin{array}{r} 9\ \blacksquare \\ +\ 3\ \ 7 \\ \hline \blacksquare\ \blacksquare\ 3 \end{array}$$

4   Add fifty thousand and five to this calculator number.

5   $\frac{3}{10}$ of the population of a new town are under the age of twenty. There are 4500 people in this age group. What is the total population of the new town?

6   Write the correct sign ($>$, $<$ or $=$) in place of each ⬤.

   a $\frac{9}{16}$ ⬤ $\frac{5}{8}$ b $\frac{3}{5}$ ⬤ $\frac{21}{50}$

7   Use the diagram to help you to solve this equation:

   $\frac{1}{3}$ of $\frac{2}{5} = \frac{⬢}{▽}$

8   $296 \times 9 = 300 \times 9 -$ ▨

9   Write the correct sign ($<$, $>$ or $=$) in place of each ⬤.

   a $7\frac{1}{4}$ ⬤ $\frac{29}{4}$ b $\frac{8}{1}$ ⬤ $\frac{40}{8}$

10 Usha's cyclometer recorded these trips: 3·6 km, 4·5 km and 10·9 km. What was the total distance travelled?

61

Give the next two numbers in each sequence.

1   1·5 , 2·0 , 2·5 , ▨ , ▨ , . . .
2   2·4 , 2·3 , 2·2 , ▨ , ▨ , . . .
3   1·4 , 1·6 , 1·8 , ▨ , ▨ , . . .
4   7·4 , 7·6 , 7·8 , ▨ , ▨ , . . .
5   1·2 , 1·5 , 1·8 , ▨ , ▨ , . . .
6   0·68 , 0·65 , 0·62 , ▨ , ▨ , . . .
7   0·05 , 0·1 , 0·15 , ▨ , ▨ , . . .
8   0·96 , 0·97 , 0·98 , ▨ , ▨ , . . .
9   2·5 , 5·0 , 7·5 , ▨ , ▨ , . . .
10 0·025 , 0·05 , 0·075 , ▨ , ▨ , . . .

62

1   Add 0·1 to   a 1·9   b 6·96
2   Add 0·1 to   a 0·007   b 0·09
3   Add 0·01 to   a 0·59   b 0·043
4   Add 0·01 to   a 9·09   b 0·99

KEEP YOUR EYE ON DECIMAL POINTS.

5	Add 0·001 to	a 0·539	b 0·47
6	Add 0·001 to	a 9·099	b 0·659
7	Subtract 0·1 from	a 5·0	b 3·99
8	Subtract 0·01 from	a 10·0	b 10·1
9	Subtract 0·001 from	a 10·0	b 1·004
10	Subtract 0·001 from	a 0·1	b 0·76

63

Look at these examples:

$$0.3 \times 4 = 1.2 \quad (\tfrac{3}{10} \times 4 = 1\tfrac{2}{10})$$

$$0.03 \times 4 = 0.12 \quad (\tfrac{3}{100} \times 4 = \tfrac{12}{100})$$

$$0.003 \times 4 = 0.012 \quad (\tfrac{3}{1000} \times 4 = \tfrac{12}{1000})$$

Find the products.

1	0.4×6	2	0.09×3
3	3×0.14	4	0.56×2
5	6×0.007	6	0.018×2
7	4 times 0·104	8	0.205×7
9	3×7.4	10	8.06×5

64

$$10 \text{ times } 0.463 = 4.63$$
$$100 \text{ times } 0.463 = 46.3$$
$$1000 \text{ times } 0.463 = 463$$

1	10 times 4·7	2	10×0.49
3	24.24×10	4	4.91×100
5	100×0.6	6	0.987×1000
7	0.43×1000	8	6.7×20
9	30×2.4	10	1.3×70

65

1   Write in digits the number which is half a million more than this calculator numeral.   **9 900 000**

2   If four times a number is increased by 12, the result is 60. What is the number?

3   Look at the numbers below. Find the sum of the numbers which are divisible by 5.

        400   656   705   501

        | 1 | 7 | 6 | 5 | 9 | 9 |

4   Above is the kilometre reading of a car. The coloured digit means tenths of a kilometre. Write in words the kilometre reading after the car has travelled another 40·1 kilometres.

5   A racing driver covered 10·5 km in 3 minutes. What was his average speed in kilometres per minute?

6   There are 30 books on a library shelf. $\frac{2}{3}$ of the books are science books and $\frac{3}{4}$ of the science books are about electricity. How many books are about electricity?

7   The number in the denominator of a fraction is twice as great as the number in the numerator. If the fraction is in its lowest terms, what is the fraction?

8   Solve this equation: $\frac{5}{8}$ of **n** = 35.

9   Write the statement below in full.

    $\frac{\blacksquare}{100} = 1\cdot01$

10 What fraction of this shape is coloured:

      a yellow?   *b* red?   *c* blue?

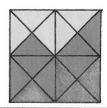

66

$0\cdot3 \times 0\cdot6$	$= 0\cdot18$	$\frac{3}{10} \times \frac{6}{10} = \frac{18}{100}$
tenths × tenths	⟶ hundredths	
$0\cdot3 \times 0\cdot06$	$= 0\cdot018$	$\frac{3}{10} \times \frac{6}{100} = \frac{18}{1000}$
tenths × hundredths	⟶ thousandths	
$0\cdot03 \times 0\cdot06$	$= 0\cdot0018$	$\frac{3}{100} \times \frac{6}{100} = \frac{18}{10\,000}$
hundredths × hundredths	⟶ ten thousands	

Use the table above to help you answer the questions on the next page.

Find these products.

1 0.6×0.7	*2* 0.43×3
3 0.24×0.4	*4* 0.7×0.9
5 0.21×0.4	*6* 0.06×0.04
7 0.09×0.3	*8* 0.3×0.003
9 0.9×1.1	*10* 4.2×0.7

67

$$36.7 \div 10 \qquad = 3.67$$
$$36.7 \div 100 \qquad = 0.367$$
$$36.7 \div 1000 \qquad = 0.0367$$

1 $32.9 \div 10 = \blacksquare$	*2* $407 \div 10 = \blacksquare$
3 $0.67 \div 10 = \blacksquare$	*4* $9.67 \div 100 = \blacksquare$
5 $46.8 \div 100 = \blacksquare$	*6* $0.9 \div 100 = \blacksquare$
7 $0.7 \div 10 = \blacksquare$	*8* $126 \div 100 = \blacksquare$
9 $239.4 \div 1000 = \blacksquare$	*10* $685 \div 1000 = \blacksquare$

68

There is no difficulty in dividing a decimal number by a whole number. $0.42 \div 7 = 0.06$

1 $3.5 \div 5 = \blacksquare$	*2* $4.97 \div 7 = \blacksquare$
3 $5.6 \div 4 = \blacksquare$	*4* $\dfrac{8.4}{7} = \blacksquare$
5 $49.7 \div 7 = \blacksquare$	

It is easy to divide by a decimal number.
$$0.6 \div 0.2 = 6 \div 2 = 3$$
$$2.64 \div 2.4 = 26.4 \div 24 = 1.1$$
In each of these examples the divisor has been made into a whole number.

6 $3.6 \div 0.6 = \blacksquare$	*7* $2.43 \div 0.03 = \blacksquare$
8 $0.45 \div 0.09 = \blacksquare$	*9* $4 \div 0.2 = \blacksquare$
10 $8 \div 0.5 = \blacksquare$	

69

1   Round off to the nearest whole number:

      a 32·49   *b* 19·09   *c* 0·61

2   4·75 × 1000

3   3 × ⬛ = 2·1

4   0·1 of 0·1 = ⬛

5   4·7 + 0·47 = ⬛

6   3·9 × ⬛ = 39

7   300 × 0·06 = ⬛

8   15 ÷ 0·1 = ⬛

9   5 − 4·15 = ⬛

10 What is the difference between 0·3 and 0·03?

HOW MUCH HAVE YOU LEARNED?

70

1   Write in digits the number that is forty thousand more than this calculator numeral.

2   Find the sum of 17, 16, 14, 13 and 30.

3   Look at this equation: 694 − 387 = 307.

Now work out these subtractions.

      a 20 694 − 16 387 = ⬛   *b* 694 − 486 = ⬛

4   An aircraft flew at an average speed of 1800 km/h for $2\frac{1}{2}$ hours. How far did it fly?

5   48 is $\frac{3}{4}$ of what number?

6   Martin gave $\frac{2}{5}$ of his 20 stamps for 6 of Sarah's. How many stamps does Martin have now?

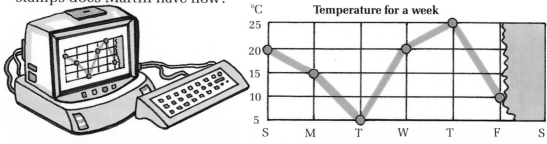

7   The daily average temperature for the week was 15°C. What was the temperature on the Saturday?

8

      Remember $0·5 = \frac{1}{2}$

Now find this product: 178 × 0·5.

9   What is the average of 3·4, 4 and 1·6?

10 A satellite orbits the Earth every 90·11 minutes.

In how many minutes does it complete a hundred orbits?

71

1. How many twos are the same value as 14 fives?
2. How many tens are the same value as 9 fifties?
3. How many fifties are the same value as 60 fives?
4. How many tens are the same value as 7 fifties?
5. How many twos are the same value as 196 pennies?
6. How many twenties are worth 16 fives?
7. How many fives are equal in value to £1·60?
8. How many fifties are equal in value to £23·50?
9. Change 60 fives to pounds.
10. Change 70 twenties to pounds.

72

1. Change 55 tens to pounds and pence.
2. Change 50 fifties to pounds.
3. 49p = 9 fives + ▢ twos.
4. £0·85 = 4 tens + ▢ fives + 5 twos.
5. £7·70 = 30 twenties + ▢ tens.
6. £3·06 = 5 fifties + ▢ twos.
7. ▢ tens + 6 pennies = £1·76.
8. ▢ fives + 17 twos = £0·69.
9. 14 tens + 4 fives + ▢ twenties = £2·40
10. 4 fifties + 4 tens + 4 fives = £ ▢.

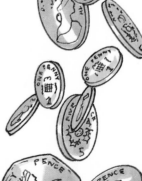

73

1   What is the cost of the torch and the jigsaw?
2   What is the cost of the torch and the metal puzzles?
3   What is the cost of the torch and the colour set?
4   What is the cost of the jigsaw and the metal puzzles?
5   What is the cost of the metal puzzles and the colour set?
6   How much would be left out of £1 after buying the torch?
7   How much would be left out of a fifty after buying the jigsaw?
8   How much would be left out of a ten and two fives
    after buying the metal puzzles?
9   How much would be left out of a fifty after buying the colour set?
10 How much more does the torch cost than the metal puzzles?

74

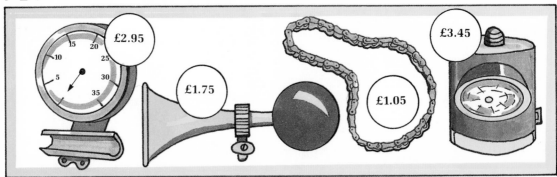

1   If £4 was spent on two articles, what were they?
2   What is the total cost of the speedometer and the horn?
3   What is the total cost of the horn and the headlamp?
4   What change would be received from £2 after buying a chain?

5   What change would be received from £5 after buying the speedometer?
6   How much more is the headlamp than the horn?
7   How much more is the speedometer than the horn?
8   I had £5·50 change from £10. Which two items did I buy?
9   What is my change from £10 after buying the two most expensive items?
10 What is my change from £5 after buying the two cheapest items?

75

1   Write in words the numeral 70 070 000.
2   What is the greatest whole number that can be put in place of ■ to make the sentence below true?

$$30 \times ■ < 280$$

3   A school received one thousand five hundred pencils. If they were packed thirty to a box, how many full boxes were there?

4   What fraction of the shape on the right is blue?

5   Find the average of these scores: 17, 13, 6, 4, 12 and 8.
6   Write an equation for this problem then find the solution. *Seven more than twice a number is 23. What is the number?*
7   Write out this equation in full: $6 = \frac{▲}{3}$.
8   Arrange the numbers below in order of size from the least to the greatest.

        0·45   4·5   0·045   45·0

9   Solve this equation: $n - 3·6 = 3·4$.
10 A garage put 60 litres of petrol in a new car. The petrol gauge then showed $\frac{3}{4}$ full. How many litres does the tank hold when full?

76

1   $43p + 16p + 17p = ■\,p$
2   $16p + 38p + 62p = £\,■$
3   $£0·70 + £0·90 = £\,■$
4   $£0·80 + £0·67 = £\,■$
5   $£0·60 + £0·75 + £0·40 = £\,■$
6   $£4·50 + £0·76 = £\,■$

7   £3·95 + £0·69 = £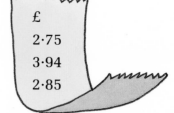

8   £1·35 + £2·70 + £0·65 = £ ▮

9   £4·60 + £3·25 + £1·75 = £ ▮

10   £9·98 + £7·47 + £1·02 = £ ▮

77

1   £1·00 − £0·37 = £ ▮   2   £10·00 − £0·70 = £ ▮

3   £3·50 − £0·90 = £ ▮   4   £2·30 − £1·40 = £ ▮

5   £1·00 − £0·05 = £ ▮   6   £7·80 − £0·85 = £ ▮

7   £4·75 − £0·90 = £ ▮   8   £2·00 − £0·46 = £ ▮

9   £3·03 − £0·73 = £ ▮   10   £10·50 − £0·60 = £ ▮

78

1   £4·70 + £ ▮ = £7·20

2   £9·30 − £ ▮ = £2·60

3   £3·58 + £ ▮ = £5·00

4   £ ▮ + £3·65 = £10·00

5   £1·76 + £ ▮ = £3·10

6   £7·10 + £ ▮ + £2·80 = £10

7   £10·00 − £ ▮ = £4·76

8   £ ▮ + £9·80 + £0·60 = £11·00

9   £20 − £ ▮ = £0·69

10   £ ▮ + £8·43 = £10·40

79

1   What change would you have if you spent £1·05 out of £5·00?

2   What is the total of this till receipt?

£

2·75

3·94

2·85

3   Take £0·75 from £2·70.

4   What is the difference between £0·07 and £7·00?

5   If I had £1·10 more, I would have £11·00. How much do I have?

6   Shubi bought items costing £0·50, £0·55 and £0·45.
    What change did she have from £5?
7   What must be added to £3·30 to make £30?
8   £0·33 + £0·44 + £0·55 = £ ☐
9   To the sum of £7·65 and £2·35 add the difference between these amounts.
10 Emma bought a diary costing £1·15. She gave the assistant a £5 note. Her
    change was made up of 6 fifties and the rest in fives.
    How many fives were in the change?

80

1   Write in digits a numeral for ten and a half million.
2   Replace ◯ with >, < or = to make the sentence below true.
        $0·75$ ◯ $\frac{30}{40}$

3   Write the date on the Lincoln Memorial in our numerals.

4   The sum of three consecutive whole numbers is 24.
    What are the numbers?

MCMXXII

5   (16 × 25) + ☐ = 1000
6   A coach driver averaged 50 kilometres per hour on a 2000 kilometre tour.
    How many hours of driving time did the tour take?
7   The pie chart on the right shows the favourite sport
    of the boys in a school. If there are 240 boys
    in the school, how many:

Favourite sport

football, tennis, swimming, cricket

        a prefer football?   b prefer swimming?
8   By what number must 4·9 be multiplied to obtain a product of 490?
9   £10·40 + £7·60 + £0·99 = £ ☐
10 David had £1 to spend. He bought a model aircraft, a tube of glue and a tin
    of paint. How much change did he receive?

55p   25p   17p

81

1   14p × 3 = ▓ p

2   £0·09 × 8 = £ ▓

3   £0·18 × 5 = £ ▓

4   21 × 5p = £ ▓

5   40 × 7p = £ ▓

Use the graph to
find these costs.

6   15 articles at 10 for 12p

7   25 articles at 10 for 12p

8   5 articles at 10 for 12p

9   8 articles at 20 for 45p

10 How many articles
    at 20 for 45p can be
    bought for 18p?

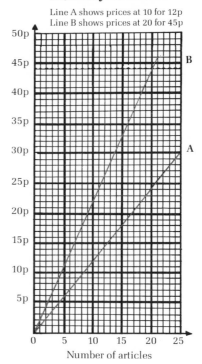

A ready reckoner

Line A shows prices at 10 for 12p
Line B shows prices at 20 for 45p

Number of articles

82

A school ordered the following sports equipment. Find the cost of each item.

1   2 footballs

2   6 tennis rackets

3   3 cricket bats

4   5 hockey sticks

5   8 badminton rackets

Now do these.

6   £4·40 × 7 = £ ▓

7   £3·90 × 3 = £ ▓

8   £0·50 × 116 = £ ▓

9   £1·50 × 84 = £ ▓

10 £0·25 × 36 = £ ▓

83

1 Karen earned £1·80 for 3 days holiday work. How much was this per day?
2 David paid in 8 equal payments for a science set costing £10.
   How much was each payment?
3 £1·50 ÷ 6 = ☐ p
4 Find $\frac{1}{8}$ of £1·04.
5 £1·53 ÷ 9 = £ ☐
6 Share £3·80 equally among 4 boys. How much does each boy get?
7 £6·00 ÷ 20 = £ ☐
8 £44·40 ÷ 6 = £ ☐
9 £1·30 ÷ 5 = £ ☐
10 What is two-thirds of £4·20?

84

1 How many 20p stamps can be bought for £20·00?
2 How many tennis balls at 90p each can be bought with £5·40?
3 How many pencils at 9p each can be bought with £1·08?
4 Marbles are 10 for 7p. How many can Sam get for £0·56?
5 A textbook costs £3·10. How many of these textbooks can be bought for £31?

6 How many of the T-shirts shown in the picture
   could I buy for £22·50?

7 Emma collected £2·10 by selling concert
   tickets at 35p each. How many tickets did she sell?
8 David saved 25p each week until he had £6·50.
   For how many weeks did he save?

9 How many of the records on the right
   could be bought with £25·20?

10 Science books cost £3 and nature study books £2·50. How many more nature
   study books than science books can be bought with £15?

85

1   Write in digits the number that is ten more than nine hundred and nine thousand, nine hundred and ninety-nine.

2   David weighs 32 kilograms and Robin 41. Karen weighs 27 kilograms and Sarah 37. How much more do the boys weigh than the girls?

3   $(29 \times 8) + 8 = \blacksquare$

4   What number is represented by ⬤⬤⬤ in this subtraction?

$$\begin{array}{r} 8\ 0\ 6 \\ -\ \text{⬤⬤⬤} \\ \hline 1\ 0\ 9 \end{array}$$

5   $500 - 0.05 = \blacksquare$

6   $\frac{1}{2}$ of $\frac{3}{8} = \frac{\text{⬤}}{\text{◆}}$

7   A church appealed for a million pennies. How much is this in pounds?

8   60p is made up of an equal number of tens and twos. How many coins are there altogether?

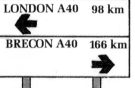

LONDON A40   98 km

BRECON A40   166 km

9   How far is it from London to Brecon?

10 Ann wishes to buy a Microscope Set. She has 10 fifties and 10 fives. How much more does she need?

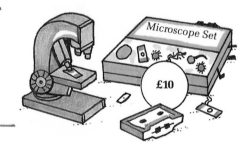

Microscope Set

£10

86

If we know the cost of 1, it is easy to find the cost of 10 or 100 or 1000.
Study the examples below.

1 stamp costs £0·20.	10 stamps cost £2·00.
1 stamp costs £0·20.	100 stamps cost £20·00.
1 stamp costs £0·20.	1000 stamps cost £200·00.

Now try these.

1   If 1 costs £0·09, 10 cost £ $\blacksquare$.

2   If 1 costs £0·80, 10 cost £ $\blacksquare$.

3   If 1 costs £0·17, 10 cost £ ■.

4   If 1 costs £0·03, 20 cost £ ■.

5   If 1 costs £0·30, 30 cost £ ■.

6   If 1 costs £0·06, 100 cost £ ■.

7   If 1 costs £0·40, 400 cost £ ■.

8   If 1 costs £0·07, 1000 cost £ ■.

9   If 1 costs 4p, 1000 cost £ ■.

10   If 1 costs 85p, 1000 cost £ ■.

87

If we know the cost of 10 or 100 or 1000, it is easy to find the cost of 1.
Study the examples below.

10 stamps cost £2·30.	1 stamp costs £0·23.
100 stamps cost £23·00.	1 stamp costs £0·23.
1000 stamps cost £230·00.	1 stamp costs £0·23.

Now try these.

1   If 10 cost £0.80, 1 costs £ ■.

2   If 10 cost £7·00, 1 costs £ ■.

3   If 10 cost £4·50, 1 costs £ ■.

4   If 20 cost £0·40, 1 costs £ ■.

5   If 20 cost £6·00, 1 costs £ ■.

6   If 30 cost £0·90, 1 costs £ ■.

7   If 100 cost £4·00, 1 costs £ ■.

8   If 200 cost £80·00, 1 costs £ ■.

9   If 1000 cost £90·00, 1 costs £ ■.

10   If 2000 cost £40·00, 1 costs £ ■.

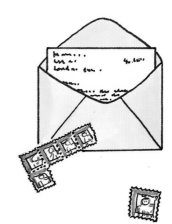

88

1 m 16 cm

Ali's stretch is one metre sixteen,
that is: 1 metre and 16 centimetres.
1 centimetre is $\frac{1}{100}$ metre = 0·01 metre.
16 centimetres is $\frac{16}{100}$ metre = 0·16 metre.
Ali's stretch is **1·16 m**.

Write these measurements in metres.

1   1 metre and 45 centimetres   2   9 cm

3   700 cm   4   2 metres and 40 centimetres

5   4 m 3 cm   6   30 cm

7   128 cm   8   706 cm

9   1 m 22 cm   10 6 m 10 cm

89

> **Remember!** When zeros are added to the right
> of a decimal number, the value is not changed.
> **1·2 m = 1·20 m = 1·200 m**

Write these measurements in centimetres.

1   1·07 m   2   3·73 m

3   5·40 m   4   1·4 m

5   9 m 60 cm   6   0·5 m

7   0·04 m   8   17·65 m

9   0·30 m   10 7·7 m

90

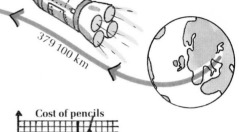

379 100 km

1 Lunik 2 travelled to the moon. How many kilometres less than half a million did it travel?

2 Use the graph on the right:

     a to find the cost of 6 pencils.

     b to find how many pencils can be bought for 28p.

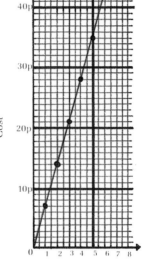

Cost of pencils

Cost

Number of pencils

3 I am thinking of a number. $\frac{7}{8}$ of the number is 49. What is the number?

4 $\frac{70 \times \blacksquare}{2} = 1400$

5 $\frac{1}{2} - \frac{\blacktriangle}{8} = \frac{1}{4}$

6 The sum of two fractions is $\frac{15}{16}$. If one of the fractions is $\frac{5}{8}$, what is the other?

7 The product of 36 and 8 is the same as the product of 16 and $\blacksquare$.

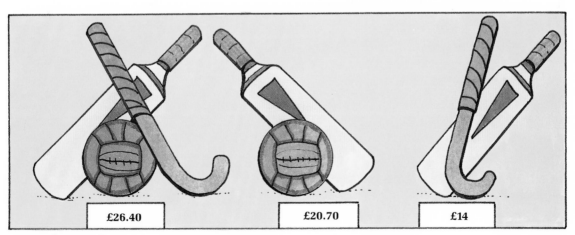

£26.40   £20.70   £14

8 What is the price of the football?

9 What is the price of the hockey stick?

10 What is the cost of the cricket bat?

91

Very small measurements are made in **millimetres (mm)**. The length of this rectangle is **3 cm** or **30 mm**.

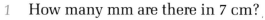

1   How many mm are there in 7 cm?

2   How many mm are there in $4\frac{1}{2}$ cm?

3   How many mm are there in 80 cm?

4   66 mm = ▢ cm ▢ mm

5   370 mm = ▢ cm

6   17 cm 9 mm = ▢ mm

7   23 cm = ▢ mm

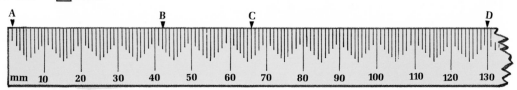

8   Find the distance between A and B:

      a   in mm,

      b   in cm and mm.

9   Find the distance between A and C:

      a   in mm,

      b   in cm and mm.

10   Find the distance between B and D:

      a   in mm,

      b   in cm and mm.

92

1000 millimetres = 1 metre

> **1 mm = one thousandth of a metre = 0·001 m**

$$43 \text{ mm} = \frac{43}{1000} \text{ metre} = 0\cdot043 \text{ m}$$

$$178 \text{ mm} = \frac{178}{1000} = 0\cdot178 \text{ m}$$

Write the measurements below in metres.

1   629 mm

2   74 mm

3   6109 mm

4   8 mm

5   32 000 mm

Write the measurements below in mm.

6   4·693 m

7   0·046 m

8   0·005 m

9   8·703 m

10   17 m

93

The distance from A to B is 36 mm.

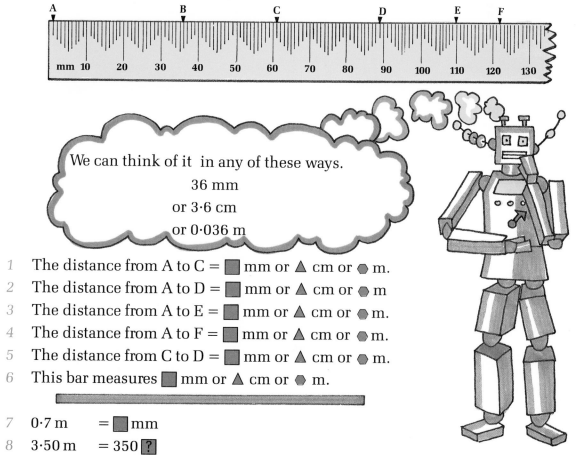

We can think of it in any of these ways.

36 mm

or 3·6 cm

or 0·036 m

1   The distance from A to C = ▨ mm or ▲ cm or ⬣ m.

2   The distance from A to D = ▨ mm or ▲ cm or ⬣ m

3   The distance from A to E = ▨ mm or ▲ cm or ⬣ m.

4   The distance from A to F = ▨ mm or ▲ cm or ⬣ m.

5   The distance from C to D = ▨ mm or ▲ cm or ⬣ m.

6   This bar measures ▨ mm or ▲ cm or ⬣ m.

7   0·7 m   = ▨ mm

8   3·50 m   = 350 ?

9   4·9 cm   = ▨ m

10 7·15 m   = ▨ mm

94

> **4 m and 25 cm = 4·25 m**

Replace 'and' in the measurements below by using the decimal point.

1. 2 m and 73 mm
2. 3 m and 29 cm
3. 1 m and 124 mm
4. 12 m and 5 cm
5. 0 m and 85 mm

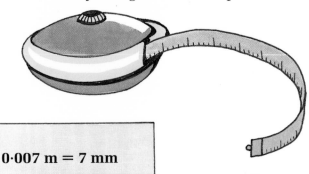

> **0·007 m = 7 mm**

Write these measurements using whole numbers.

6. 2·75 m
7. 0·006 m
8. 47·51 m
9. 0·93 m
10. 3·4 cm

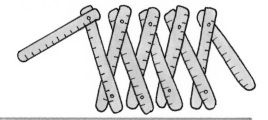

95

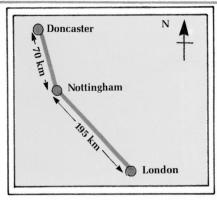

1. What is the distance from London to Doncaster and back?
2. $(120 \times 8) + (130 \times 8) = $ ▨
3. Solve this equation: $3 \times \boldsymbol{n} = 5 \times 24$.
4. Last season the school A team scored twice as many goals as the B team. Together they scored 72 goals. How many goals were scored by the A team?

5 Write the correct symbol (>, < or =) in place of ⬤.

$\frac{7}{8}$ ⬤ $\frac{3}{4} + \frac{1}{8}$

6 A number which is equal to the sum of its own factors, including 1 but excluding itself, is called a **perfect number**.

For example, 6 is a perfect number (6: 1, 2, 3, $\cancel{6}$)

Which of these is a perfect number?

16 20 28 11

7 Last week the kilometre recorder on Usha's bicycle showed 278·8 km. The reading is now 300 km. How far has Usha cycled?

8 $100 - 74·85 - 0·15 = $ ◼

9 $5 - 0·05 = $ ◼

10 £0·85 was made up of an equal number of tens, fives and twos.
How many coins were there altogether?

96

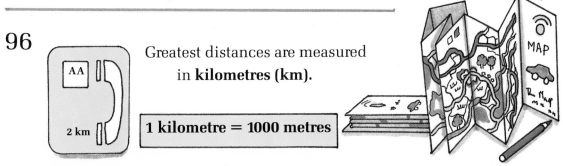

Greatest distances are measured in **kilometres (km).**

1 kilometre = 1000 metres

1 9 km = ◼ m
2 $3\frac{1}{2}$ km = ◼ m
3 2 km and 405 m = ◼ m
4 17 km 7 m = ◼ m
5 5 km 50 m = ◼ m
6 10 000 m = ◼ km
7 4800 m = ◼ km ▲ m
8 7030 m = ◼ km ▲ m
9 8005 m = ◼ km ▲ m
10 6309 m = ◼ km ▲ m

97

7 metres ↔ 0·007 km
436 metres ↔ 0·436 km
78 metres ↔ 0·078 km

1 Write 247 m in km.
2 Write 703 m in km.
3 Write 29 m in km.
4 Write 4500 m in km.

5 Write 13 km 2m in km.

6 $\frac{3}{4}$ km = ■ m

7 0·850 km = ■ m

8 0·7 km = ■ m

9 6·15 km = ■ m

10 What is the distance in metres to Bolbec?

BOLBEC →

3·4 km

98

1 2·5 m × 4 = ■ m

2 7 km − 2270 m = ■ km

3 9 km ÷ 100 = ■ m

4 70 mm × 1000 = 70 [?]

5 38 cm ÷ 10 = 38 [?]

6 423 m ÷ 100 = 423 [?]

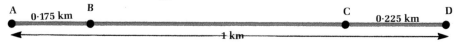

A   0·175 km   B   C   0·225 km   D

1 km

7 What is the distance in metres from B to C?

8 4·5 cm × 100 = ■ cm or ▲ m

9 3·65 m × 1000 = ■ m or ▲ km

10 3·6 m ÷ 100 = ■ m or ▲ cm

99

1 When the car was driven into a garage there was a space of 55 cm in front and 45 cm in the rear. What was the length in metres of the garage?

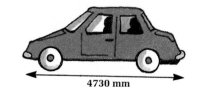

4730 mm

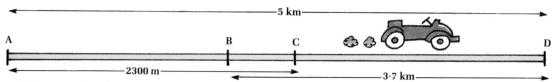

5 km

A   B   C   D

2300 m   3·7 km

2 What is the distance from B to C?

3 The shortest length of timber I can order is 1·8 m. The next size is 300 mm longer. What is this size in metres?

4 If 3·65 m is cut off a length of 20 m, what length remains?

5 How many 40 cm lengths of string can be cut from the ball of string on the right?

100 m

6 A cyclist has already covered 24 km. This is $\frac{3}{4}$ of the distance she has to travel. How far does she still have to cycle?

7   Find the cost of 0·25 m at £3 per metre.

8   Find the cost of 0·9 m at £5 per metre.

9   Find the cost of 0·83 m at £1 per metre.

10 Find the cost of 60 cm at £1·20 per metre.

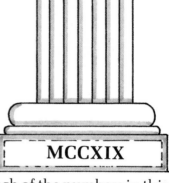

100

1   Write in digits the number three hundred million.

2   Write this date in our numerals.

> **MCCXIX**

3   Find the number, excluding 1, which is a factor of each of the numbers in this set (common factor).

   [52,   91,   143]

4   David gave away three-quarters of his stamps. He still has 350 left. How many did he give away?

5   $39 \div 1000 = 0·$ ■

6   The cyclist in the picture completed 8 circuits. How far did she cycle?

> **CIRCUIT**
> **1·750 km**

7   $\frac{3}{8} + \frac{1}{4} =$ ■

8   A school bought 48 ballpoint pens at 3 for 50p. What was the total cost?

9   1·50 m of wire costs 24p. How much is this per metre?

10 Work out the cost of 0·75 m at £1·24 a metre?

101

> We have already learned that we can calculate the **perimeter** of a square by multiplying the number of units in a side by 4.
>
> perimeter (15 × 4) mm = 60 mm

15 mm

Find the perimeter of these squares.

1   side 11 mm: perimeter = ■ mm

2   side 30 cm: perimeter = ■ m

3   side 200 m: perimeter = ■ m

4   side 0·5 km: perimeter = ■ m

5   side 1 km and 500 m: perimeter = ■ m

Figures in which all sides are the same length are said to be **regular**.

6   Find the perimeter of this triangle.

7   Find the perimeter in metres of this hexagon.

8   Find the perimeter in cm of this pentagon.

9   Find the perimeter in m and cm of this rhombus.

10   The perimeter of a square is 0·5 km. What is the length in metres of a side?

102

The perimeter of this rectangle can be found by measuring the length and breadth, then calculating the perimeter, like this:

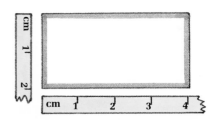

$$(4 + 2) \times 2 = 12 \text{ cm}$$

Measure the length and the breadth of each of these rectangles and calculate the perimeter of:

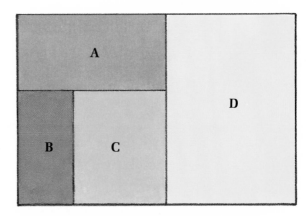

1   rectangle A.

2   rectangle B.

3   rectangle C.

4   rectangle D.

Find the perimeters.

5 length 24 cm	width 16 cm	perimeter ▢ cm
6 length 75 cm	width 65 cm	perimeter ▢ m
7 length 114 mm	width 86 mm	perimeter ▢ cm
8 length 0·85 m	width 0·35 m	perimeter ▢ m
9 length 1·45 m	width 5 cm	perimeter ▢ m
10 length 83·5 m	width 21·5 m	perimeter ▢ m

103

1 kilogram (kg) = 1000 grams (g)

1·327 kg = 1327 g

4785 g = 4·785 kg

1 3 kg = ☐ g
2 1·439 kg = ☐ g
3 0·678 kg = ☐ g
4 0·095 kg = ☐ g
5 2·007 kg = ☐ g

6 2649 g = ☐ kg
7 783 g = ☐ kg
8 74 g = ☐ kg
9 2040 g = ☐ kg
10 3 g = ☐ kg

104

4620 g = 4·620 kg or 4·62 kg
3200 g = 3·200 kg or 3·2 kg

1 7450 g = ☐ kg
3 2040 g = ☐ kg
5 4500 g = ☐ kg
7 4·08 kg = ☐ g
9 0·88 kg = ☐ g

2 3800 g = ☐ kg
4 700 g = ☐ kg
6 3·7 kg = ☐ g
8 9·003 kg = ☐ g
10 0·096 kg = ☐ g

105

1   Write in words the number that is a hundred times
    greater than a hundred thousand.

2   The population of a city is 640 000 and that of a neighbouring city 460 000.
    What is the total population of the two cities?

3   Ann paid £7·25 for a table tennis bat and 6 balls. If the bat cost £6·05,
    what did she pay for each ball?

4   What fraction of this figure is:

    a white?

    b yellow?

    c red?

5   Write this equation in full: $\frac{2}{3} = \frac{8}{\blacksquare}$

6   $132 \times 0.25 = \blacksquare$

7   Write the next two numbers in the sequence below.

    2·72, 2·81, 2·9, 2·99, $\blacksquare$, $\blacksquare$.

8   Here are five bunches of bananas. What is the average
    number of bananas in a bunch?

9   $\frac{80 \times \blacksquare}{2} = 1600$ 10 $7 \div 0.1 = \blacksquare$

106

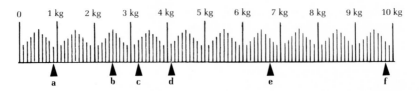

What is the weight in kilograms and grams shown by the pointer at:

1   **a**?   2   **b**?   3   **c**?

What is the weight in kilograms shown by the pointer at:

4   **d**?   5   **e**?   6   **f**?

What is the total weight in kilograms of each of these?

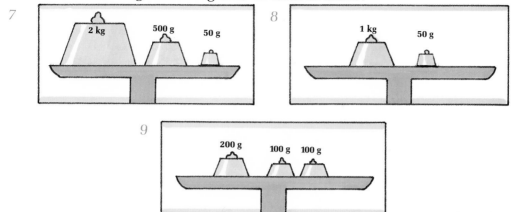

7

8

9

10 **Net weight** means the weight of the contents. Look at the pictures below. What is the net weight in grams of the contents of the jar?

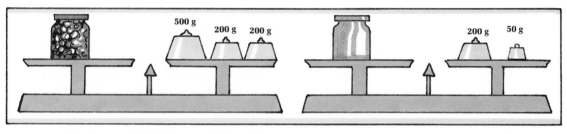

107

The weight shown at **(a)** is 100 g or $\frac{1}{10}$ kg or 0·1 kg. Write in grams, then as a fraction, then as a decimal of a kilogram the weight shown at:

1 **(b)**   2 **(c)**   3 **(d)**

Find the cost of:

4   500 grams at £1·76 per kg.

5   100 grams at £12·50 per kg.

6   200 grams at £1·35 per kg.

7   250 grams at £1·40 per kg.

8   750 grams at £1·20 per kg.

9   125 grams at £2·40 per kg.

10   900 grams at £2 per kg.

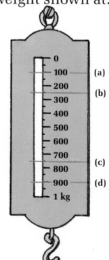

108

Greatest weights are measured in **tonnes.**

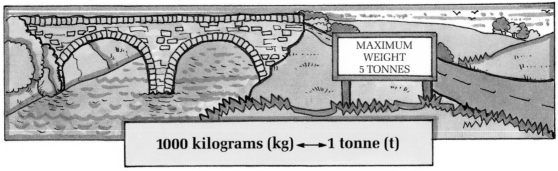

1000 kilograms (kg) ←→ 1 tonne (t)

1   7030 kg = ■ t ▲ kg
2   4250 kg = ■ t ▲ kg
3   3100 kg = ■ t ▲ kg
4   7007 kg = ■ t ▲ kg
5   4167 kg = ■ t

Write these in kilograms.

6   9 t and 700 kg
7   3 t and 60 kg
8   7 t and 9 kg
9   4·75 t
10 6·957 t

109

1   250 kg × 10 = ■ t
2   80 kg × 50 = ■ t
3   6 t ÷ 4 = ■ kg
4   3 t − 1200 kg = ■ t ▲ kg
5   2 t − 650 kg = ■ t ▲ kg
6   What is the total weight in tonnes of eight large crates, each weighing 250 kg?
7   3 t 650 kg + 2 t 550 kg = ■ t ▲ kg
8   2 t 400 kg ÷ 6 = ■ kg
9   4100 kg − 2 t and 600 kg = ■ t
10 A loaded lorry weighs 6·5 t. The empty lorry weighs 2800 kg. What is the weight in kilograms of the load?

110

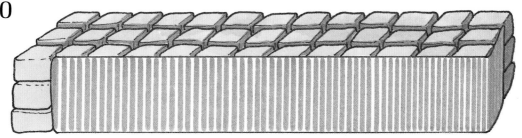

1   How many tablets of soap are there?

2   What fraction of a pound is this amount of money?

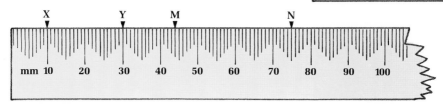

3   What is the distance between:

      a **X** and **Y** in cm?

      b **M** and **N** in m?

4   $4{\cdot}9 + 16{\cdot}32 + 1{\cdot}1 = \blacksquare$

5   Write $\frac{24}{48}$ in its simplest form (lowest terms).

6   Solve this equation: $8 \times 9 = 12\,\boldsymbol{x}$.

7   $28 \times 1{\cdot}25 = \blacksquare$

8   $70 - 0{\cdot}077 = \blacksquare$

9   The sale price of an electronic game is £15·50. If this is two-thirds of the usual price, how much is saved?

10   What fraction of the circle on the right is:

      a coloured?

      b white?

111

1 How many seconds are there in $3\frac{1}{4}$ minutes?

2 How many seconds are there in $\frac{2}{5}$ of a minute?

3 Change 330 seconds to minutes.

4 $3\frac{1}{3}$ minutes = ▢ s

5 10 min 10 s = ▢ s

6 How many minutes are there in $1\frac{2}{3}$ hours?

7 How many minutes are there in $1\frac{1}{5}$ h?

8 545 min = ▢ h ▲ min

9 195 s = ▢ min ▲ s

10 The drawing shows part of the face of a stopwatch which measures to one-tenth (0·1) of a second. The time shown by the hand at **A** is 23·9 s. What is the time shown by the hand at **B**?

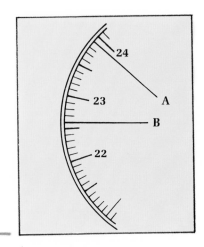

112

How many minutes are there between these times?

1 7.05 am and 8.00 am

2 9.43 am and 10.05 am

3 6.56 am and 7.18 am

4 11.19 pm and 12.11 am

5 12.15 pm and 1.13 pm

How many hours and minutes are there between these times?

6 17 minutes past 4 in the afternoon and half past 6 in the evening.

7 8 minutes past 7 in the evening and 5 minutes past 10 in the evening.

How many seconds are there from:

8 **A** to **B**?

9 **A** to **C**?

10 **B** to **C**?

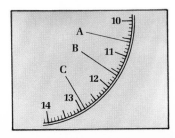

113

Rail, bus and airline timetables use the **24-hour clock**.

3.00 am is written 03 00   3.00 pm is written 15 00.

3.57 am is written 03 57   3.57 pm is written 15 57.

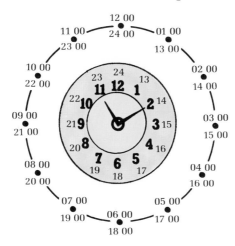

Give the 24-hour clock time for:

1   five past eight in the evening.

2   seven o'clock in the morning.

3   11.50 pm.

4   twelve o'clock midday.

5   five minutes before midnight.

Change these to 12-hour clock times using am and pm.

6   07 10   7   20 00   8   10 00

9   13 30   10   00 40

114

1   In 1980 the population of Slough was ninety-six thousand five hundred. How many less than 100 000 was this?

2   What is the greatest odd number you can name with these digits?

3   I am thinking of a number. If 7 is added to $\frac{1}{5}$ of the number, the answer is 55. What is the number?

4   Solve this equation: $\frac{360}{5} = 8 \times$ ▪ .

5 What is the weight in kg and g of
£10 worth of bronze coins?

6 $\dfrac{72 \times 40}{80} = \blacksquare$

7 $1007 \div 25 = \blacksquare \, r \, \triangle$

8 A javelin throw at an international sports meeting was 60 m 60 cm. What was this in centimetres?

9 What change would be received from a £5 note after buying two of the fountain pens shown on the right?

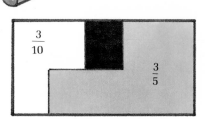

£1.95

10 What fraction of this shape is black?

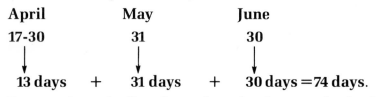

$\dfrac{3}{10}$

$\dfrac{3}{5}$

115

How many days are there from:

17th April to 30th June?

April	**May**	**June**
17-30	**31**	**30**
↓	↓	↓
13 days +	**31 days** +	**30 days** = **74 days**.

Do not count the first day unless the dates are **inclusive**.

Work out the number of days from:

1 10th January to 7th February.

2 20th February (not a leap year) to 18th March.

3 17.2.84 to 18.3.84.

4 17.4.85 to 18.5.85 inclusive.

5 30th July to 30th September inclusive.

	July	August	September	October
Sun	5 12 19 26	2 9 16 23 30	6 13 20 27	4 11 18 25
Mon	6 13 20 27	3 10 17 24 31	7 14 21 28	5 12 19 26
Tue	7 14 21 28	4 11 18 25	1 8 15 22 29	6 13 20 27
Wed	1 8 15 22 29	5 12 19 26	2 9 16 23 30	7 14 21 28
Thu	2 9 16 23 30	6 13 20 27	3 10 17 24	1 8 15 22 29
Fri	3 10 17 24 31	7 14 21 28	4 11 18 25	2 9 16 23 30
Sat	4 11 18 25	1 8 15 22 29	5 12 19 26	3 10 17 24 31

You may use the calendar above to help you with these questions.

Work out the number of days from:

6   4th July to 1st September.

7   7th August to 4th October.

8   28th July to 1st October.

9   14th August to 14th October.

10   1st July to 31st October inclusive.

116

These are the distances travelled by this coach.

1st hour 60 km

2nd hour 43 km

3rd hour 47 km

in 3 hours 150 km

average speed 50 **kilometres per hour (km/h)**

Work out the average speed in km/h.

1   116 km in 2 h

2   45 km in $1\frac{1}{2}$ h

3   42 km in $3\frac{1}{2}$ h

4   55·5 km in 3 h

5   70 km in 1 h 45 min

Work out these speeds in km/h.

6   45 km in 10 min

7   7 km in 12 min

8   18 km in 40 min

9   100 metres in 30 seconds

10   An express left Edinburgh at 11 00 and arrived in London at 16 00, a journey of 630 km. What was the average speed of the train in km/h?

117

speed of car 60 km/h
distance in 5 hours 60 × 5 = 300 km

1   A cyclist travelled at an average speed of 20 km/h for $2\frac{3}{4}$ hours. How far did he cycle?

Work out the distance travelled in:

2   45 min at 24 km/h.

3   1 h 40 min at 30 km/h.

4   35 min at 60 km/h.

5   2 h 30 min at 96 km/h.

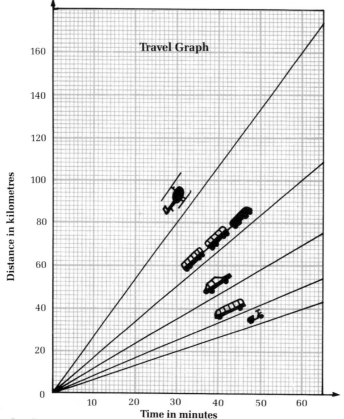

Use the graph above to answer these questions.

6   What was the speed in km/h of the helicopter?

7   What was the speed in km/h of the car?

8   What was the speed in km/h of the coach?

9   What was the distance travelled by the train in $\frac{1}{2}$ hour?

10   How long did the scooter take to travel 20 kilometres?

118

> **distance** 35 km
> **speed** 15 km/h
> **time** $\frac{35}{15} = 2\frac{1}{3}$ h = 2 h 20 min

1 A helicopter flew a distance of 225 km at an average speed of 150 km/h. How long did the journey take?

Work out the time taken on each of these journeys.

2 $22\frac{1}{2}$ km at 15 km/h   3 17 km at 60 km/h

4 23 km at 30 km/h   5 50 km at 40 km/h

6 Travelling at 5 km/h, how long will it take to go 1 km?

7 Travelling at $7\frac{1}{2}$ km/h, how long will it take to go 1 km?

8 Travelling at 24 km/h, how long will it take to go 1 km?

9 What speed in km/h is 7 km in 12 min?

10 What speed in km/h is 5 km in 3 min?

119

1 Solve this equation: $1000 - n = 370 + 405$.

2 A number is divisible by 9 if the sum of its digits is divisible by 9. Which of the numbers below are divisible by 9?

　　4375　　9854　　4068　　77 760

3 Write the date on the right in our numerals.

4 $\frac{165 \times 11}{15} = \blacksquare$

5 £5·25 × 16 = £ $\blacksquare$

MDCCXL

6 What change would be received from £5 after buying 3 books at £1·60 each?

7 36 × 0·75 = $\blacksquare$

8 What fraction of this set is not red? Write the fraction in its lowest terms.

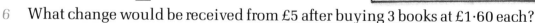

9 Find the average weight.

　　6 kg　　7·85 kg　　1·15 kg

10 The glass holds 25 ml. How many times can it be filled from a full bottle?

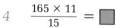

120

We have already learned that the best unit shape
to use for surface measurement (area)
is the square.

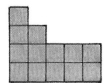

The area of this shape is 13 square
units when ▪ is the unit.

Find the area of these shapes when ▪ is the unit.

1 　　2 　　3 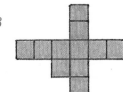　　4

The area of this shape is **one square centimetre (cm²)**.
Small areas are usually measured in square centimetres.

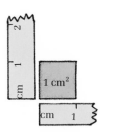

Find the area in cm² of these shapes.

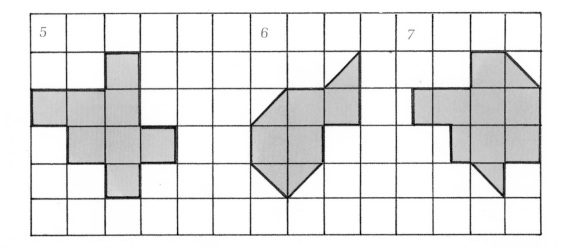

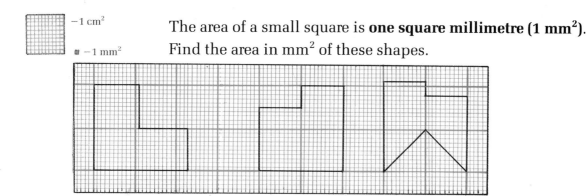

−1 cm²

−1 mm²

The area of a small square is **one square millimetre (1 mm²)**.
Find the area in mm² of these shapes.

121

We can calculate the area of rectangles without counting each square.

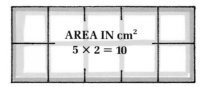

AREA IN cm²
5 × 2 = 10

Measure the number of cm in the length and breadth of the rectangles below and calculate the areas.

1

2

3

Calculate the area of the rectangles below:

  a in cm².
  b in mm².

4

5

Complete these.

6   Length 40 cm, breadth 9 cm, area ■ cm².

7   Length 60 mm, breadth 20 mm, area ■ mm².

8   Length 40 mm, breadth 30 mm, area ■ cm².

9   Length 7·5 cm, breadth 20 cm, area ■ cm².

10   Find the area in mm² of a square with sides of 10 cm.

122

Larger areas are calculated in **square metres (m²)**.

1   Calculate the area of a rectangular garden 40 m by 20 m.

2   Work out the area of a square with sides of 13 m.

3   A square lawn has a perimeter of 80 m. What is its area?

4   What is the area of a floor 8·7 m by 10 m?

5   A rectangular garden has an area of 1000 m² and a width of 25 m. What is the length of the garden?

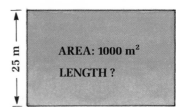

25 m   AREA: 1000 m²
         LENGTH ?

6   A rectangle has an area of 600 cm². If the length of the rectangle is 40 cm, what is the breadth?

7   A carpet has an area of 10·5 m². If it is 3 metres wide, how long is it?

8   A square has an area of 121 m². What is its perimeter?

Land is measured in **hectares (ha)**.

1 hectare = **10 000 m² (100 m × 100 m)**

SALE
FARMLAND
200 hectares

9   A rectangular field measures 200 m by 150 m. What is its area in hectares?

10   Very large areas are measured in **square kilometres (km²)**. How many hectares are there in 1 km²?

123

We use a square as a unit measure for area. We can use a cube as a unit measure for **volume**.

Taking this as the cubic unit,

we can see that the volume of this block is 10 cubic units.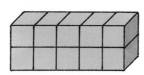

How many cubic units are there in each of these?

1

2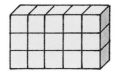

3

We can calculate the volume of this shape. There are 10 cubic units in each layer and there are 4 layers.

$$5 \times 2 \times 4 = 40$$

Calculate the volume of each of these.

cubic unit

4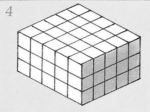

5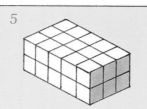

6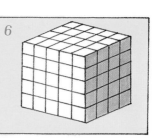

Taking as the cubic unit, find the volume of each of the boxes below.

7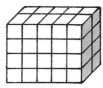

8

9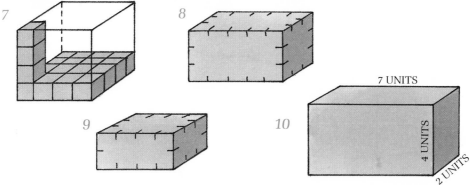

10

7 UNITS

4 UNITS

2 UNITS

124

1 Round off 89 463 790 to the nearest million.

2 Two hundred and forty foreign stamps were shared equally among some
children. If they had 48 each, how many children were there?

3 $14\,x = 28$, so $\frac{28}{x} = \blacksquare$

4 4 is a **square number**. $2 \times 2 = 4$
9 is a **square number**. $3 \times 3 = 9$
Which of the numbers below are square numbers?
   400   64   1000   810

5 How much for all these apples?

3 for 40p

APPLES

6 How much did a school pay for 20 library books at £3·50 each?

7 Find the missing terms in each of these pairs.
   $a \quad \frac{2}{3} = \frac{\blacksquare}{18}$ $b \quad \frac{6}{5} = \frac{30}{\blacksquare}$

8 A school high jump record is 1·61 m. How many
centimetres short of 2 m is this?

9 What is the weight of the fruit juice in the picture below?

10 What is the distance in kilometres and metres from Dinton to Mingford?

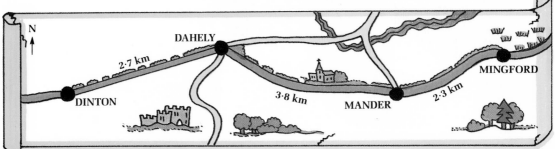

125

Here is a **cubic centimetre (cm^3)**.

Now calculate the **volume** in cubic centimetres of the figures below.

1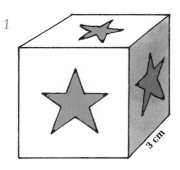

2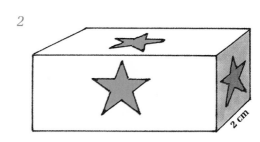

Find the volumes in cm^3 of these boxes.

3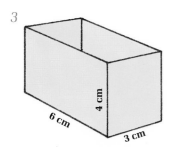

4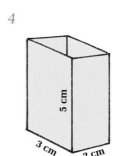

5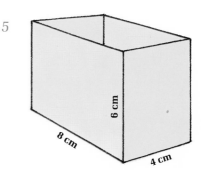

Calculate the missing measurements of these boxes.

6   Length 10 cm, width 3 cm, height 5 cm, volume ▢ cm^3

7   Length 4 m, width 5 m, height 6 m, volume ▢ m^3

8   Length 10 m, width 3 m, height 1 m, volume ▢ m^3

9   Length 7 cm, width 2 cm, height ▢ cm, volume 28 cm^3.

10   Length ▢ m, width 3 m, height 4 m, volume 60 m^3

126

1 litre (ℓ) = 1000 millilitres (ml)

1   2020 ml = ▨ ℓ ▲ ml
2   4400 ml = ▨ ℓ ▲ ml
3   How many ml are there in $1\frac{3}{4}$ ℓ?
4   How many 5 ml doses of medicine are there in a $\frac{1}{4}$ ℓ bottle?
5   0·023 ℓ = ▨ ml
6   1250 ml = ▨ ℓ
7   600 ml = ▨ ℓ
8   How many 300 ml bottles can be filled from 6 ℓ?
9   2500 ml = ▨ ℓ
10   6·050 ℓ = ▨ ℓ ▲ ml

127

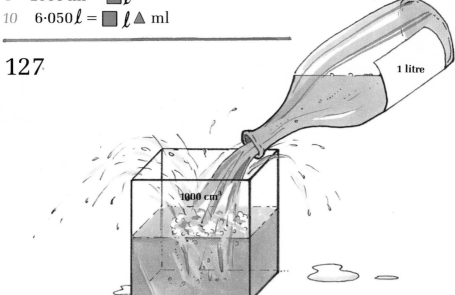

1 litre

1000 cm³

1   We know that 1000 cm³ takes up the same space as 1 litre.
    What space does 1 ml take up?

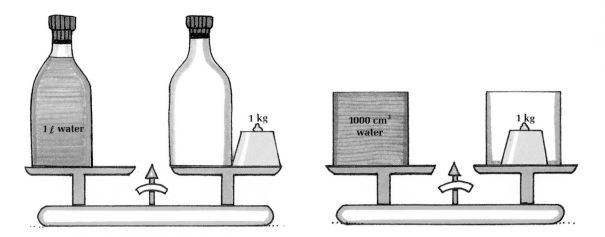

2   What is the volume in cm³ of a bottle that holds 300 ml of water?

3   A vase has a volume of 750 cm³. What part of a litre of water can it hold?

4   A tank is 1 m by 1 m by 1 m. How many litres of oil can it hold?

5   What is the weight in kg of 1·5ℓ of water?

6   What is the weight in grams of 0·5ℓ of water?

7   A litre bottle is half full of water and weighs 1120 g. What is the weight of the empty bottle?

8   A fish tank full of water weighs 12·850 kg. The empty tank weighs 2·35 kg. What is the capacity of the tank in litres?

9   An empty bottle weighs 200 g. What is its weight when it holds 0·5ℓ of water?

10   What is the weight in grams of $\frac{3}{4}$ ℓ of water?

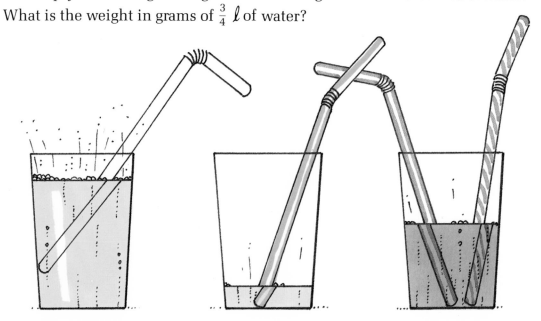

There is a short way of writing certain multiplications such as
7 × 7 × 7, when the same factor is repeated.

$\overbrace{\qquad}^{\text{3 factors}}$

For 7 × 7 × 7 we can write 7^3.

For 4 × 4 × 4 × 4 × 4 we can write 4^5.

The little raised numeral is called an **index** and indicates the number of factors.

For 2 × 2 we write 2^2; we say '2 to the second power'
or '2 squared'.

For 2 × 2 × 2 we write 2^3; we say '2 to the third power'
or '2 cubed'.

For 2 × 2 × 2 × 2 we write 2^4; we say '2 to the fourth power' or '2 to the 4th'.

Write these products using index notation.

1   9 × 9 × 9 × 9 × 9 × 9 = ■

2   5 × 5 × 5 × 5 × 5 × 5 × 5 × 5 = ■

3   10 × 10 × 10 × 10 × 10 = ■

Give each of the following with factors written out in full,
like this:

$$9^3 = 9 \times 9 \times 9$$

4   8^3 5 6^4 6 10^5

Solve these equations.

7   $4^3 = n$ 8 $9^2 = x$

9   $3^3 = b$ 10 8 × 8 × 8 × 8 = 8^c

129

$$10^5 = 10 \times 10 \times 10 \times 10 \times 10 = 100\ 000$$
$$10^4 = 10 \times 10 \times 10 \times 10 = 10\ 000$$
$$10^3 = 10 \times 10 \times 10 = 1000$$
$$10^2 = 10 \times 10 = 100$$
$$10^1 = 10$$
$$10^0 = 1$$

It is simple to write a numeral so that every place value is a power of 10, like this:

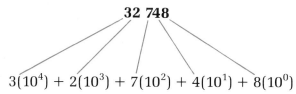

32 748

$$3(10^4) + 2(10^3) + 7(10^2) + 4(10^1) + 8(10^0)$$

Write a numeral in index notation for each of these.

1	87	2	326
3	5285	4	8741
5	38 256	6	100 100
7	341 000	8	400 404
9	7 631 428	10	9 090 000

130

1 Write this numeral
   using index notation.

2 a $\dfrac{700 \cdot 007}{100}$ =  b 700·007 × 10 = ▪

3 $1\frac{1}{3} \div 2$ = ▪

4 A snack bar has 10 full trays of eggs.
   How many eggs are there?

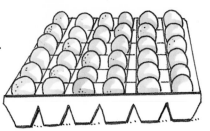

5 If $x = 4$, $y = 5$ and $z = 0\cdot5$,
   then 2 xyz = ▪.

6 £0·25 × 64 = £ ▪

7 Diamonds are weighed in **carats**. A carat is 0·2 g.
   How many 1 carat diamonds would make up a kg?

8 Taking ▱ as the cubic unit,
   what is the volume of this stack?

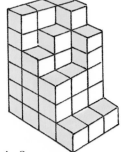

9 What is the speed in km/h of 150 m/min?

10 A brick weighs 1500 g. What is the weight in tonnes of a thousand bricks?

131

1 How many half millions are there in 50 000 000?

2 Work out the total value of these coins.

Value of coins	50p	20p	10p	5p	2p	1p
Number of coins	50	50	50	50	50	50

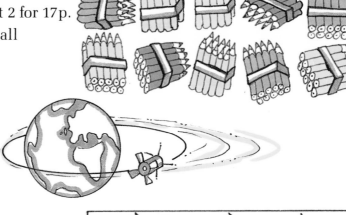

3   These pencils are sold at 2 for 17p.
    What is the total cost of all
    the pencils?

4   Distance: 105 000 km
           Speed: 30 000 km/h
    Time taken: ■ h ▲ min

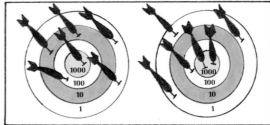

5   Speed: 28 000 km/h
           Time: 1 h 15 min
        Distance: ■ km

6   What fraction of all the
    darts is in the 1000 ring?
    Write the fraction in its
    lowest terms.

7   a   What is the area of the red region?
    b   What is the area of the blue region?

8   How many millilitres of paint
    are there in all?

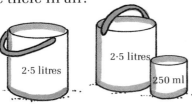

2·5 litres   2·5 litres   250 ml

9   What is the average temperature?

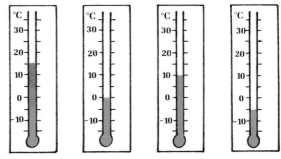

10 A strip of plastic $3\frac{1}{2}$ m long is cut into 7 equal lengths.
    What is the length in mm of each piece?

132

1   How many more than 99 999 is a million?

2   $222 \times 5 =$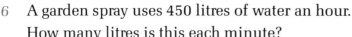

3   Subtract eight hundred thousand from 8 088 756.

4   £0·80 × 500 = £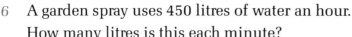

5   This pie chart shows the favourite colours of 30 pupils.

      a How many pupils voted for yellow?

      b How many pupils chose red?

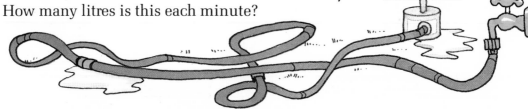

6   A garden spray uses 450 litres of water an hour.
    How many litres is this each minute?

7   A cyclist completed the final stage of the Tour de France
    in 2 h 10 min at an average speed of 36 km/h. What was the distance?

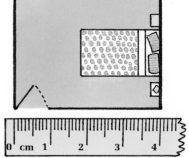

8   The scale of this plan is 1 cm to 1 m.
    The length of the bedroom is 4 m.
    What is the area in m² of the room?

9   If a litre of oil weighs 0·91 kg, how many litres are there in 3·64 kg of oil?

10 A train's correct time of arrival was 11 55. The train arrived $\frac{3}{4}$ hour late. At
    what time did the train arrive? Use the 24-hour clock system.

133

1 Write this date in our numerals.

MCMXXIV

2 $4800 \div 50 =$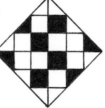

3 Find the total of £0·55, £5·05 and £5·50.

4 The Eiffel Tower is 300 metres in height. How many metres less than one-third of a kilometre is this?

5 Sarah was born on 22nd January 1980. Her cousin, Emma, is 35 days older. What was the date of Emma's birth?

6 How many 0·9 litre bottles can be filled from a container holding 45 litres of fruit juice?

7 What fraction of this shape is:
   a black?
   b white?

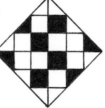

8 A square field has a perimeter of 802 m. What is the length in metres and centimetres of a side?

9 A thousand bricks weigh 2450 kg. What is the weight in kg of one brick?

10 This drawing shows part of a stopwatch which measures one-tenth (0·1) of a second. How many seconds are there from **A** to **B**?

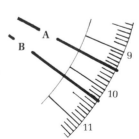

134

1   $(100 \div 1) + (100 \times 1) + (100 + 1) + (100 - 1) =$ ▢

2   Write the numeral for the number that is 50 million more than 50 000.

3   What is the change from a £20 note after spending £9·87?

4   This bar chart shows the amounts collected by three girls for Save the Children Fund. How much was collected altogether?

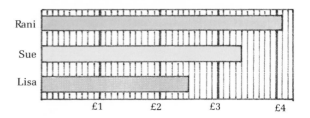

5   What fraction of this square is:
      a   coloured blue?
      b   coloured red?

6   1 cm on this map represents 50 km. What is the actual distance covered by a helicopter that flew from Plymouth to Southampton, then to Bristol and on to Cardiff?

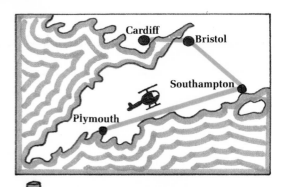

7   What is the total quantity in litres of this fruit cocktail?
      $\frac{3}{4}\,\ell$ pineapple juice
      650 ml grapefruit juice
      600 ml ginger ale

8   What is the volume in cubic units of this solid? Use ▢ as the cubic unit.

9   What is the cost of a kilogram of ground almonds at 80p for 125 g?

10   What is the speed of 10 metres per second in kilometres per hour?

135

1 The distance around the Earth at the Equator is 40 000 kilometres. How many times around the Earth at the Equator is equal to a million kilometres?

Safety Quiz

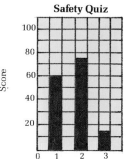

2 The graph shows the three scores of Park School in a Safety Quiz. What was the average of the scores?

3 660 006 − 6000 = ▢

4 $(5 \times 10^3) + (5 \times 10^2) + (5 \times 10^1) + (5 \times 10^0) =$ ▢

5 $(£7{\cdot}77 \times 60) + (£7{\cdot}77 \times 40) = £$ ▢

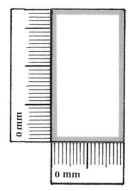

6 a What is the perimeter in mm of this rectangle?
   b What is the area in cm² of this rectangle?

7 Almonds cost £6 per kg. What is the cost of 125 g?

8 How long would it take a champion cyclist to cover 8000 m at an average speed of 40 km/h?

9 A train left Paddington at 23 20 and arrived at Reading $\frac{3}{4}$ hour later. What was the time of arrival at Reading?

10 a Of these dots, what fraction in its lowest terms is red?
   b Of these dots, what decimal fraction is white?

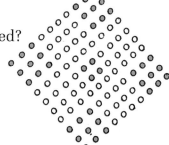

136

1 Write the number that is three hundred thousand greater
   than 7 777 951

2 Subtract 5 from ten thousand and four.

3 1 111 111 101 ÷ 9 =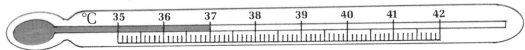

4 About what was the population of Upton in:

    a 1935?

    b 1975?

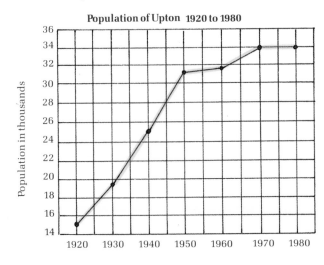

Population of Upton 1920 to 1980

5 *a* 0·009 × ▣ = 9·0

  b 50 ÷ ▣ = 0·5

6 750 millilitres of cooking oil cost 90p. How much is this per litre?

7 This fish tank measures 40 cm long,
   20 cm wide and 20 cm high.
   What is its volume in cm³?

8 750 g of nuts were taken from a bag holding $1\frac{1}{4}$ kg. How many grams were left?

9 A cruise liner sailed 10 000 nautical miles. What is this distance in
   kilometres? (nautical mile → 1·852 km)

10 During his illness Bob's temperature rose 2·2° above normal
   (normal body temperature is 37° C). Then his temperature dropped 1·7°.
   What was his temperature then?

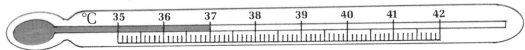